Lisanne,

MW00638252

Anthology
Long Island Authors Group

Love,
Mom
7/2022

ANTHOLOGY

Copyright 2022 by the Long Island Authors Group

All rights reserved

No part of this book may be reproduced or transmitted
in any form or by any means, electronic or mechanical,
including photocopying and recording, or by any information
storage or retrieval system, except in writing from the
publisher. Requests for permission can be made by visiting our
website at www.longislandauthorsgroup.org.

p. cm.

ISBN: 978-0-9989714-7-6

Authors, American-Fiction--New York (State)--Long Island.
Essays-Selection--New York (State)--Long Island. Poets--New
York (State)--Long Island.
Literary Collections--New York (State)—Long Island.

Savage, Marianne
Title: Illustrator

Published by
Long Island Authors Group
Long Island, New York

DEDICATION

To those brave enough to put their words to print.

ACKNOWLEDGEMENTS

President Dr. John Krahn – who motivated
the members to participate in the Anthology

The Authors – who submitted their work

JoAnn Krapp and Linda Maria Frank – who were
the project managers and co-editors of Anthology

Marianne Savage – who was illustrator
and graphic designer for Anthology

JoAnn Krapp – whose beautiful watercolor
graces the front cover

The Volunteers – who edited and proofread

PROLOGUE

How does any project get started? Someone sees a need. An opportunity presents itself. Or a delightful idea of producing something of worth takes form.

Belonging to a community of authors offers many opportunities. There are fairs where they can showcase and sell their works to the public. There are lectures and guest speaker spots to present ideas and information. There are social events to enjoy each other's company and exchange experiences.

What is missing is the vehicle to share the literary talents.

In 2022, when our group reached a milestone, our fifteenth anniversary, our president, John Krahn, suggested we celebrate by producing a literary publication that showcases the diverse talents of our members. An invitation was sent out, citing guidelines for publication, Over the course of two months, forty-two original, unpublished works were received, edited and proofread, ready for publication. And so ... ANTHOLOGY was born.

Unbeknownst to JoAnn Krapp and Linda Frank, innocent in their pursuit of publishing their own books, the task of birthing the Anthology was bestowed on them.

So, to work.

Marianne Savage, author and illustrator of children's books as well as graphic designer and illustrator, took on the role of formatting the Anthology. Together with JoAnn Krapp, who by the way, is a talented water colorist, covers were produced, the interior was organized, and ANTHOLOGY, Long Island Authors Group came together.

Each author has a story, and each is unique. In many cases there is an agreement to where the human experience takes us.

Although ANTHOLOGY is a source of pride and enjoyment, it also has the practical value of presenting the talents of our members to the public in yet another format.

No more talk.

Turn the pages and enjoy the stories; funny, poignant, hard, mysterious, ethereal, spiritual, real-life, practical, serious, lyrical, enlightening, personal, wise, unbelievable, and above all entertaining.

Linda Maria Frank

JoAnn Krapp

Marianne Savage

Volunteers who Edited and Proofread

TABLE OF CONTENTS

FICTION

POETRY

NON-FICTION

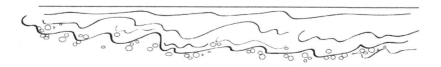

fiction

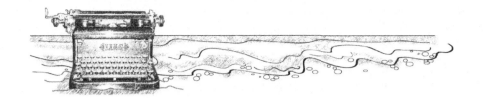

DEATH OF A MARINER

by

Roland Allnach

For five generations, the Mariner's family had worked the sea. When he was young, he remembered standing beside his father, the boat's wheelhouse doors open, a cool autumn breeze gusting through as they tacked to drag their nets. Whether the sun shone crisp and clear above them, diffuse with orange flame upon the horizon, or muted to a threatening steel gray beneath low clouds, his father would nod as his weathered face creased about his seaman's gaze.

"Rough seas ahead, son," he would say under his breath. "Rough seas ahead."

The Mariner was left to carry the family legacy after his father was caught in a net and dragged beneath the waters. He wore no life-saving gear, taking his risks as they came, drinking past the fear when he knew dangers might come and drinking more past the trauma of dodging

1

another threat. His father was a gambler and laughed when he'd come home penniless after losing a catch's earnings. No matter how much the Mariner's mother yelled, his father only let go a sigh. All the noise, all the sorrow, all the tears, they all went to silence when she left, all went to darkness when his father was dragged under in his last lost gambit.

The sea was not the Mariner's choice. As a boy he thought he loved the ocean. As a youth he craved its elusive solitude, but as a man he had no interest in the clank and shout of a catch in progress, the merciless sun beating upon salt-crusted backs in the summer heat, the insidious chill of ice fog in the early winter cold. No, all that held his interest was the quiet of a lonesome night-watch at the wheel, the motor unheard beneath him, the stars above, darkness everywhere around and between. Then his heart would beat a little slower, a little deeper, and he would part from the boat, the ocean, and leave it all behind. Where he went, he never knew, but all he needed to know was that it was out there, somewhere, a calm stretch of welcoming waters--

The quiet patch.

Rough seas behind. It was the only whisper to soothe his distemper with a life he didn't desire.

Lacking any other guidance, he followed the

dispositions of the dock rats that formed what he knew of a social circle. Their inclinations were shallow and immediate. He waved off any aspirations, choosing instead to drown his disillusionment in petty distractions. The more he realized he had become his father's son, the deeper he sank.

Rough seas ahead, son. Rough seas ahead.

A tired cycle assumed dictate over his life. He was drunk one night, collided with a sea tramp waitress in the back of his pickup, and found out he was to be a father. Under her will to keep the child, he had to pay for his sloppy seed. He put on a second-hand suit and staggered into the local magistrate.

He quaked before the marriage certificate. It wasn't a newlywed's tribulation that seized him, but the dawning realization of what was to come. The quiet patch drifted away to the impenetrable distance. He said his *I do* though he certainly *did not*, and his shoulders cramped with the unwanted burden that closed upon him like some giant clam.

Life, he came to feel, was no different than the tide. To his uneducated mind it was a revelation. The life he knew as a boy returned to him as a man, only the roles had changed. Oblivious to any other option, he settled into his father's footsteps. There had never been a choice in his life, after all. Five generations had worked the sea so he, too, would work the sea. His father was a dissolute fool so he, too, would be a dissolute fool. His mother was a drunk. pickled in the frustration of her life so in turn he watched his wife shrivel to a cadaverous strip of flesh.

The divorce came as no surprise. His mother had left his father and, though he was too young to recall anything in the way of divorce talk, he came to know it in full. His father would yell that he'd head out to Widow's Shoal and court the beckoning sea nymphs that awaited all men who worked the sea. His mother said it was fool's talk, the fantasy of a drunken sot too dizzy from swells to know real from unreal. The misery, though, was real enough.

So, too, the Mariner found his turn in such affairs. Lawyers, papers, judges; it was a different sea in which to drown, an impenetrable dark ocean he had no care nor capacity to understand much less heed its demands. The blur came in sudden focus on only one point, and that was the judge's decree: that the Mariner's boat be sold to settle financial requirements.

He was half drunk when the ruling was read. His outburst was something he heard in the distance as he became witness to his own folly. No one cared when he protested that he couldn't earn without the boat. He cursed the judge. The contempt levy mattered little. He had no money. He had no boat. He had no way to reach the quiet patch.

It wasn't a simple matter of having nothing. He realized he had become nothing.

That night, vicious with drink, he clambered aboard the boat. Five generations of misery rumbled beneath him as he gunned the throttle and headed out to sea beneath the stars. Most of all, he remembered standing in the wheelhouse with his father, the doors open, the cool breeze shifting as they tacked to drag their nets.

He buried the throttle, spun the wheel, and shredded the old boat's hull across the jagged peaks of Widow's Shoal.

The boat shuddered beneath him, but he stood resolute at the wheel. When the motor sputtered and drowned, he held his place. When the boat listed, still he held his place. When water lapped at his feet, he at last donned his flotation vest and let the ocean's chill envelope him. To his disappointment, there were no sea nymphs to lament his expected demise.

He didn't care to live, but he cursed the ocean and its nymphs. Despite his hate, his mariner's wisdom saved him, knowing full well the currents would wash him back to port. Half dead, half frozen, he was brought ashore. The sea had spat him out.

The disdain, at least, was mutual.

Without a boat, without money, without direction, there was only one choice. He was a Mariner, so he drifted.

Life brought him to a fishing village on a vast northern lake. He had but one skill. Hate it as he might, it was a source of support and even his meager measure of esteem refused to let him beg for food. His living was simple, his means modest, so he existed. He found lodging in the back of a warehouse overlooking the lake. At night he would stare at the stars, caught in the illusory realm between sleep and consciousness, imagining that he still owned a boat and that the quiet patch awaited him. He could see it, where the setting sun and the tranquil swells of evening merged into one crystalline, reflective band separating the world that is from the world that would never be.

What little he had, he spent on food, drink, and his lodging. He watched the rain, he loathed the cold, and he despised the thick layers of snow. On the cliffs above the lake, near his lodging, he watched as the lake winds roared up the sheer heights during winter storms to build towering masses of accumulated snow. The winter, he heard, was an unusual one, bitter cold and shattering old records.

When it seemed the season would never end there was a shift in the air, the winds changed, the temperature surged above the freezing point, and he fell asleep to the sound of a violent thunderstorm. What woke him, though, was not the roar of the tempest, but an awful creaking groan, as if the planet itself were pained. Then came a roaring crash. He had barely sat up when a wall of water blasted through the warehouse. He fell into the torrent, a violent wave spawned by a massive wall of accumulated snow that broke from the cliffs and crashed into the lake below. The water would have claimed him had not his strong fisherman's hands constricted about his air mattress. It was no life raft, but it served enough to keep him above the fatal grinding depths of shattered timber and debris.

He was found in the morning among the chaotic aftermath. Upon sight of the devastation, it was hard to imagine he had survived. Some called it miraculous, but he knew better. In the past he had cursed the sea and it spat him upon the land. Now he had cursed the lake and it too had spat him ashore.

Fed up with the cold, he once again took to drifting. Amid those delirious days he wondered if anyone was looking for him to make good on his divorce payments. The judge had said something about his responsibility after the family boat sank. There was insurance money he never claimed. Most of all in those moments he wondered about his son and what had happened to the boy—now a young man, by even loose reckoning. Perhaps the boy was better off split from the Mariner's fate of misery. Perhaps he, like the Mariner, had been hopelessly infused with the miserable call of water and was spending his life in fruitless pursuit of the same quiet patch the Mariner sought.

In the most lonesome times, the Mariner hoped his son didn't think of him at all, for there was nothing left to ponder.

Empty seas ahead, son. Empty seas ahead.

Chance one day deposited him at the end of a bar in some forgotten town. He rummaged in his pockets to find the last few dollars to his name and paid for his precious alcohol. The place was a haunt for the bystanders of Life, the lost and broken, who talked of nothing more than lost dreams and bemoaned their decrepit existence.

The Mariner laughed. He knew what those castaways desired. *The quiet patch.* It was a fool's delusion, he knew, a hope trapped in isolation among the stormy seas, a treacherous seduction sung by devious sea nymphs. Everywhere man could go, the Mariner shouted, he was framed by water. It had no care. It had no conscience. All it sought was to fill its black depths with the hopes of men.

No one paid heed to his discourse, but his laughter was more than could be tolerated. They beat him within an inch of his life and threw him in a pond, shouting that he could drown in the water he hated so much if he thought their misery was so funny.

Yet the Mariner's instinct came to his aide once again. He rolled on his back to float. The pond wasn't deep at all. He stood in its muck, staggered ashore, and flopped on a mud bank, where he was found under a swarm of mosquitoes. He was taken to a hospital and received a pauper's care. As a victim of violence, a sheriff came and questioned him. The Mariner was too dazed to think about not giving his name. The next day the sheriff told him he was wanted as a deadbeat dad.

He was not sent to jail. Instead, and to his disbelief, on the last day of his hospital stay, a young man came to visit. When the Mariner's sight cleared around this unexpected intruder, he felt a pain worse than anything he knew from the beating he suffered. Despite the man's suit, despite his clean-cut look, there was no mistaking him as the Mariner's son.

The Mariner's throat went dry.

His son had been afforded a decent upbringing with the boy's maternal grandparents. He graduated law school.

Over the years, he had tried to find the Mariner and left open inquiries on national databases for unpaid divorce settlements. After abandoning hope, there came an unexpected phone call.

It took effort to look at the boy. *The man*. A life the Mariner could not understand. "I have no money," he snapped. "I'm a drunk."

His son was steadfast. "I wanted to see you."

"That's it? Here I am."

His son crossed his arms over his chest. "At least now I know."

"Yeah? What could you know?"

His son frowned. "That there's nothing left to find."

The Mariner looked away. "Only the quiet patch," he whispered.

He closed his eyes. When he opened them, the chair was empty. It was just as well.

A local church provided him clothes and a few dollars. He signed some papers, ignored everything said to him, and walked away.

That night, nestled under a tree to sleep along an empty country road, he thought of his boy and the moment in the hospital. Who was that ingrate to pass judgment?

10

Had the boy known anything of the waters the Mariner plied, he would've shut his mouth, stayed away, considered the Mariner forgotten, and made his own attempts to chart the quiet patch.

Fool. Stupid fool. Doesn't he know?

His father's words came to him.

Rough seas ahead, son. Rough seas ahead.

Then the Mariner wept and cursed himself, for even there in the lonesome night under a tree along an empty country road, water had found a way to sting his eyes.

******

I am the Mariner. I drift. I've lost my course.

Years of drink and isolation, years of dislocation from the one thing he knew—the sea—and his inescapable hatred of its abstract waters eroded his sanity. In his dreams he was in the wheelhouse, crowded among the ghosts of his forebears as he struggled to turn the family boat away from Widow's Shoal and a beckoning sea nymph. In his nightmares, his son told him stories of a life without a father and how his maternal grandfather sought to fill a void that seemed bottomless.

Sometimes the Mariner wondered if his mother and his wife could meet independent of time to know each other in their mutual youth. Dislocated in such a way they

11

could be free of the Mariner and his cursed lineage. He saw the two women bathed in happiness, kept vital in the clinging guise of youth. At times he even saw them as lovers to escape the toxic brine of the men that destroyed their lives.

Such men were not anonymous. They were the Mariner and his father.

He wandered and hitch-hiked his way to places alien to him, alien to the life he knew, places dry and barren. Sand stung his eyes and dried his skin. Noonday glare blinded him, at once so similar and so different from the sea glare he once knew.

Yet he was no longer adrift. No, despite the aimless passage of time he at last realized some unseen hand was indeed charting his course. The old maps on the boat floated through his awareness like leaves on an autumn breeze, that same chilly air that wafted through the wheelhouse. Notes of cartography denoting the unseen depths and threatening shoals narrowed in his conscious perception. They drew together, a channel gouged by currents, water speeding in the depths to carve a path and perpetuate the currents above in an unseen handshake.

In such a way he felt his hand taken as well, a sea nymph's grip upon his wrist to take him ever further into the arid wastes that surrounded him. The nymph told him that this was how the sea floor appeared to her, where water was her air and the ocean's abyssal plain spread as a different yet similar wasteland. She told him it was a lonesome place, that vast emptiness, but it soothed her to know that somewhere beyond the depths there was something different, something more than she could know, something--

"The quiet patch," he said, extending an arm to the distance.

Yes, that's it! Her voice came to him like the soothing wash of an evening swell. *A quiet patch. That's it. Do you know what it's like?*

He shook his head as he shuffled across the burning gravel beneath his feet. "Only in my dream."

Tell me. I want to know your dream.

He clapped his hands atop his head. "I, I can't. I couldn't. I know it's there, but I don't know what it is."

Then how will you know if you find yourself there?

He stopped short. The answer was too devastating to voice.

The nymph beckoned. *Tell me. How will you know when you're there?*

He sank to his knees. One by one the edifices within

him shattered and fell to ruin. In their wake there was nothing but grief, lament for what could have been, for what he had thrown away, what he had pissed away in his ignorance.

Her eyes flashed. *How would you know?*

"I won't." He beat his fists to his forehead. "I didn't."

She laughed then, and her laughter came to him like the sound of beach shells. As they tinkled, they fell to the sand baking under a hot sun. The waters receded. Not a beach, no, a desert plain of gray gravel scorched under a merciless sun.

His hands dropped to his sides. His head rocked back. The sun blinded him.

There he sat, prostrated in oblivion, a man who had braved the mountainous waves of ocean tempests and shook his fist in defiance to their might, a man who had floated from the wreck of his boat to curse the ocean only to be spat out to safety, a man who had cursed a lake only to be spat free of its icy landslide tsunami, a man who had even cursed his tears as his own flesh and blood disowned the last vestige of his connection to the world, a man who had spent his life in unknown futile pursuit of the quiet patch he could not chart but was his to seize if he had recognized it even once as the reality he desired.

14

The Mariner would chart no further course. Like driftwood, he became a hollowed remnant. Yet the long path of his final demise was not due to the absence of the one thing he despised. The depths, the sea nymphs, the quiet patch, none held a care for the irony of men.

In the end, the Mariner's death was not for lack of water.

It was for thirst.

About the Author
Roland Allnach

A multi-award-winning author of the strange and surreal, Roland Allnach has published seven books and more than a dozen short stories. He served as LIAG president for four years, founded the LIAG Traveling Bookstore, and now manages the permanent LIAG Bookstore at the Islip Arts Council Gallery in the South Shore Mall.

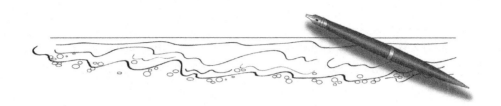

A LAST CHANCE TO BE A BOY, AGAIN

by

Jack Bilello

The man sat in the small folding chair, a chair completely inadequate for his size and girth. Glistening sweat poured profusely from every part of his body. His breath was coming in short gasps and gulps. He could listen to the sound of his heart beating in the scorching September day. How did he get here? How did he fnd himself in this predicament? How and why did he let this impending disaster happen?

He attempted to dry himself with his towel. Useless! The towel was soaking wet. Why had he brought only one towel? He slowly turned his head, casually feigning indifference. He was slightly embarrassed, for he knew his generous body extended well beyond the parameters of the folding chair. He sought her out. He found her in the crowd with the others. She was to blame. Well, not entirely, but to a large measure. For, if the truth be known,

19

there was enough blame to share with a number of people. But she was the prime mover, the instigator of the condition in which he found himself.

My God, less than a year ago, all was well with the world, and he was at peace with himself. He was a successful businessman, smugly content with the necessary "accoutrements" -wife – 1; children – 2; residences – 3 (Massapequa, Southampton, Boca); cars – 4 (two luxury, for wife and husband and two, very nice, for the kids). As a youth he had been a "superior" athlete, but that was a long time ago. Now at the age of 48, the metamorphosis was complete. He had been transformed into the classic proverbial "couch potato," a spectator, satisfying himself by watching other people having all the fun. He had spent the better part of the last 25 years "rendering unto Caesar" and, as a result, both his bank account and his waistline bulged. He had become the man other people in society wanted him to be. And after 25 years of doing what he had been doing so well, the man had made that sad transition from exciting career to job to task to chore. But that was quite alright; for by any standard of our society, he was successful.

In his life as a passive spectator, he had witnessed grown up, mature men, sometimes thirty-five to forty and beyond, behave like little children. He had only to watch on his mega-sized TV screen the final game of the World

Series, the NBA playoffs, the Super Bowl, the Stanley Cup, a grand slam tennis final, and he would see it-a spontaneous outburst of pure, joyous, unbridled ecstasy.

He would experience a brief tinge of envy, but it would pass. He knew that he could never again feel like that. It would not be possible for him to recapture that feeling ever again. The dream had died. It had perished with his last victory in stickball, punchball, sand-lot baseball, and school yard basketball. Hey, we're talking 30 odd years.

His wife, on the other hand, was another story. She had committed herself more than ten years ago to the life of an athlete. She found something she was good at and went out and did it – every day. She became a jogger. And, while she would never be a professional athlete, she derived immense satisfaction from each day's work out and her occasional entry in a marathon. Her greatest satisfaction was to compete and complete what she started. Last year, her number was finally picked for the New York City marathon, and she had finished 14,752 out of 23,000 runners who entered. The man noticed (he couldn't help noticing it, even glued to the TV) that his wife was slimmer, ate better, rarely drank, slept better, and had stopped smoking. He couldn't pinpoint a particular date and time, but it had happened gradually over the past ten years.

It was she who had badgered him for the last couple of years to "get out and get some exercise." He had resisted. But when his friends started to gang up on him, his resistance gradually eroded. Four or five of his good buddies had started playing tennis about three years earlier. Socially, they were entirely engaged by their newfound activity, and the man began to feel the pressure of subtle ostracism. Finally, he entered the arena. Suffice it to note, within a years' time, his buddies approached him to find out if he was interested in the USTA Amateur Tennis Tournament. He decided to give it a crack. It might be fun. And it was. His team cruised through the summer league. Each of his friends made a marked contribution to the team's success. While his contribution was marginal, nevertheless, it counted. His personal record was three and two, playing both singles and doubles, occasionally. He even started to lose some weight, but he had a long way to go, for he still allowed this venture into the "world of sports" to camouflage many of his dietary indiscretions.

With his team's local victory, he was invited to participate in the regional playoffs. He did not think he would actively play in any of the matches, but a teammate had injured his foot on the frst day of competition and had to withdraw from future matches.

The man was upset by this turn of events. For it meant that he was thrust into the final and decisive match – the match to decide which team was to go to the national championships. He felt totally inadequate. He blamed his teammate for the injury. Lame foot, indeed! It sounded more like lame excuse.

"Time" – oh, no! The minute and a half had transpired, quickly, all too quickly. He was down 6-5 in the third set. He really didn't want to reenter the arena. Fate would have it that his team had won two and lost two matches. The outcome rested squarely on his shoulders, and there was no escape. Win, and it's Palm Springs for the Nationals. Lose, and it's back to Massapequa and obscurity. The burden was crushing.

He rose slowly and dropped his towel. He peered at his wife and his friend among the spectators. Yes, they were the authors of his predicament. If it weren't for them, he could be home watching football on his giant screen – better than being here. His eyes focused on his teammate who had completed their matches and won. Did they look smug? He squinted at his other teammates. They had won their match but tried to convey the proper measure of humility to those who had congratulated them on their victory.

As he approached the baseline, he remembered something that one of his teammates had related. He told him a story about Teddy Roosevelt, years after he had left the presidency. Teddy had the opportunity to go on a safari to South America. He was tired, old, in ill-health, and his family begged him not to go. But, Teddy, that old Roughrider, wouldn't listen to any of that advice. He went. And he went because as he said, it was his "last chance to be a boy again."

As the man tensed to receive serve, he briefly allowed that little story about T.R. to kick up a fuss in his mind. He called time, cleared is mind and said, "Ready."

In the next twelve minutes, the man violated most of the Commandments of Tennis. He did not keep his eye on the ball all the time. He did not keep his wrist firm on the fore-hand volley. He did not prepare early on a back-hand cross- court attempt (nor change the grip). He did not bend his knees, nor follow through on a number of other shots. He did not step into the ball, nor hit off his front foot on other attempts. He did not punch a volley, nor meet the ball well out in front. He did not take small quick steps while running to hit a ball and thereby hit it on the run. And, finally, at match-point, he found himself trapped in "No Man's Land". But this novice also did much that was right. Every time, he violated a cardinal principle of tennis, he came back and did that which was "right" on the next shot. He used his primordial athletic ability, innate but long untested, to try to overcome his technical faults. In the end, he did not meet that imposter "victory", but he played with persistence, determination, and courage. He captured and conveyed the timeless dictum of Montaigne, occasionally echoed by one of his friends, "The worth and value of a man is in his heart and in his will; there lies his real honor. Valor is the strength, not of legs and arms but of heart and soul . . ." But, he lost, nonetheless. He lost after taking that final game to what seemed endless.

At match point, his opponent leaped for joy. The man's shoulders slumped and drooped. Leaping across the net, his opponent extended his hand, and the man limply shook it. He had barely finished this perfunctory ritual, when as he turned, his wife rushed to his side and embraced him.

"Never have I been more proud of you. That guy has been playing for years. He's never lost a match. You scared the hell out of him." His friend was right on her heels. He pounded the man on his back and hugged him mightily.

"What a great match to watch. You were fantastic. Next year it's Palm Springs, for sure. Only the way you're improving, you won't be able to play on our team." All his teammates engulfed him, generous and enthusiastic in their high praise for his remarkable effort. When the smoke cleared and the fuss died down, the man walked off the court arm in arm, embraced by his wife and the warm and sustained applause of the many spectators gathered to watch the outcome of the final match. They watched the man having the fun of playing and participating.

He had lost, but he had not been beaten. He had lost, but he had not been defeated. In some strange, crazy way, he had endured and prevailed.

He felt totally, completely, entirely physically and emotionally spent, drained, and exhausted. His entire body, mind and soul were as one.

He felt like a boy, again. He felt simply, wonderful.

About the Author
Jack Bilello

Jack Bilello, raised and educated in Brooklyn, lives in Massapequa Park. A former Fulbright scholar, member of Phi Beta Kappa, and retired History Chair at Lindenhurst Schools, he has authored five books, Bonds of War, American Patrol, I Still Love Joni James, Heart of a Lion, and A Piece of the Heart.

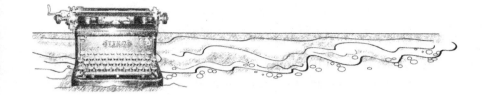

ANYBODY HOME?

by

Linda Maria Frank

The lock with the doorknob is sitting on my front porch. It's been there for a very long time. In fact, it was there before the porch sagged at such an angle that the old wicker rocker was tossed into the front yard. That happened after a rainstorm of Biblical proportions. I don't remember when. The weather events of such proportions seem to occur more and more frequently.

My vantage point of the front room windows doesn't give me a close-up view, so I suspect some part of that mechanism is stuck between two floorboards. What this means effectively is that anyone can enter and invade my home. I'm surrounded by a pine and birch forest, well off the main road, on a dirt track. Ivy has been growing all over my chimneys and roof. It makes me wonder if anyone venturing by would even discover a house so secluded and disguised by nature.

But I do have visitors. They find their way through the large chimney in my front room. I guess the bricks haven't fallen in to obstruct the flue. There's not been a fire there since before I developed the ivy problem. It's begun to pry up my shingles. I worry about a case of rot, and I become squeamish at the thought of termites. Ugh!

Now, let me tell you about the invaders, I mean visitors. The sun comes up every morning as it should and blinds me, turning the east windows to a fiercely bright gold. I feel the creaking in my various parts, door frames and windows, warped and rusted from disuse. And age. It won't be long, I think, until I'm a pile of splinters.

Ah! There she is again, the quivering, glossy red intruder, raising my hopes for some company, stirring those films and motes of dust that coat every nook and cranny of my consciousness, of my being.

Her nose inhales a breath of air that lies so deep within me, unused. She peers cautiously from the fireplace interior, ever careful of finding safe transit from one perch to another. She enters the room, setting my dust dress in motion, fanning my hopes from a flicker to a fame. Oh, how I wish for someone to inhabit me once more.

She hops gracefully from chimney to window, its broken smokey panes my eyes to the world. The eyes that search forsomeone to come and visit. What is she looking for? Her bushy tail is twitching and tight against her back.

He comes like a spore sprung from its capsule, with an acorn and a sprig of timothy hay, landing next to her on the sill. His sudden appearance causes a wonderful draft, creating another furry in all this dust, like snow rising instead of falling, sun-spangled in the morning light. The newcomer froze, poised to leap out the window, his amazing faculties sensing a ripple of something a bit off.

Oh, no. Please don't go! Suspended in those glittering particles, we three waited.

Whoosh! With a swish of those gorgeous fluffy tails and another explosion of diamond dust, the couple bounds to the hearth. Just then the sun has risen enough to peek through the trees, making my windows wink with the golden refection of my joy. A nest in my fireplace, at last, the little red creatures making me a home.

Days and nights flicker across the windows, the two red squirrels coming and going, till one day, one squirrel remains in the nest. What's wrong with her I worry. But soon, a barely audible squeaking tells me we'll be having a frisky little family soon. So intent was I on Mr. and Mrs. Squirrel that I miss the goings-on of my tiniest visitor yet, a brown mouse. So quiet and wary, it was easy to dismiss the mice as visitors. They provide little amusement for me, not like the squirrels who are more visible with their feats of daring-do.

Traffic in the front room increases as the baby squirrels grow, chasing each other in a hilarious, never-ending race to reach every perch in the room. I'm glad all my china ornaments are gone. Mr. And Mrs. S sometimes leave a trail of acorn scraps, too tempting to keep the tiny brown mouse in her hole in the baseboard.

Brownie, the mouse, her nose and whiskers twitching, scurries across my parlor floor to a board that has warped at the entry to my dining room. Ignoring the scraps, she squeezes her flexible little body through the crevice. I wonder what she is doing in there. I wonder too, where are the six other mice that show themselves when they think it's safe.

Varoomph! Varoomph! Egad, what's that?

Majestically surveying the room below a hawk has landed on the windowsill recently vacated by a baby squirrel. The hawk is high above the fireplace and the squirrels are nowhere to be seen. Perhaps the presence of the fearsome hawk explains the absence of the six mice. I don't really like that idea. This is not a hunting preserve, if you please.

Brownie appears through the crevice in the floorboards again. What's that in her mouth, a pink little something? Why, it's a baby! The hawk has made the same deduction. He is probably thinking two for the price of one.

Mother Brownie is running, hell bent for leather, with her precious cargo toward the hole in the baseboard. The hawk flexes her wings, eyes laser focused on Brownie. Body tensed, wings flapping, her talons detaching from the sill, a shriek from outside stops her. With an agile turn, she is gone. Brownie disappears into the baseboard.

Two sets of shrieks vibrate in the air outside. They are growing fainter. A mated pair headed for their nest?

The sun is dropping toward the horizon. Another day. The red squirrels have abandoned their nest for now, leaving a mess in the fireplace. Squirrels' nests hardly ever make it to those home improvement magazines for the "after" pictures.

Fallen leaves on the once pathway to the porch crackle and rustle. I feel the weight of someone on the porch. There is a screeching sound as if something is being pried loose. The door opens and I cannot believe it. A man stands just inside. The doorknob and lock rest in his hand. He has a large hump on his back, which he detaches somehow and places on the floor.

I haven't seen another human in some time. He fills the door jamb, so he must be tall. He has a dark beard and a woolen cap pulled down over his ears. His eyes are shadowed. His clothes look well-worn but clean, dark in color. He would blend well in the surrounding woods.

The man comes in, looking around, nudging at the mess in the fireplace. He moves down the hall to check out the other rooms. Water begins to run through the unused pipes, and it is a strange sensation. I chuckle to myself. Hah, the water still works.

He comes back to the open front door. I hear him call into the twilight. "C'mon. It's okay. No one lives here."

A young girl and a little boy, dark like the man, come in, wary and wide-eyed. They are dressed like the man, dark clothes, not the colorful ones children might wear. They look frightened. I wonder why. What brought them to this desolate place?

"Oh, Daddy, can we stay? I worry if a bear will eat me. Please?" The young girl holds the little boy's hand, and he says nothing, just looks around, eyes still huge.

"There's a big kitchen in the back with an old wood stove. I think I can get it going. We can spread the blankets. And there's water," the man tells the children. As he offers this promise of warmth, the two young ones sink to the floor.

"There is a fireplace in this room," the girl says.

The little boy pipes up. "No, no. You can't use it.

Look. There's a nest in it."

The man smiles a tiny smile as if he is unused to doing so. "Ivan is right. It's bad enough we don't have a home."

Well, I think to myself, maybe being here might change that.

The man continues. "The stove is safer anyway. I don't know if the chimney is blocked. Maria, look around. Maybe some blankets were left here."

"Ivan, come with me. I am scared to go alone."

The man goes to get wood and lights the stove. I hold my breath, but in a little while the house is not on fire, a surprise, and a blessing.

"Look what we found!" Ivan says in his little boy voice. The girl, Maria, is clutching an armload of blankets.

"I found them in a chest, one like Mamma had. They smell like something nice. I don't know what it is."

"Cedar," the father says. "That's why they are still in one piece. Cedar repels moths that eat blankets."

How nice it is to feel warmth in me again. I wonder if they will stay. By now it's dark. The squirrels have taken up residence in their nest. The family makes little noise in their own kitchen nest.

I hear the man say goodnight to Ivan and Maria. All is quiet and I revel in it. I whisper my goodnight to my three visitors. "Rest easy," I think.

In the distance a large boom rumbles, vibrating and rattling the same windows I welcomed the dawn with. Could it be a thunderstorm on the way? Before closing myself down, I gaze at the moonlit sky. There is a faint red glow on the horizon. I have never seen that before.

I gathered my ivy cloak around me and settled for the night; the third step creaked, the spare room door shut, and one of the roof timbers let out a snap.

For now, someone is home. I hope they can stay for a little while at least, until they must leave, to go who knows where, to find another home.

About the Author
Linda Maria Frank

A retired science teacher, Linda turned her talent to writing mystery stories for young readers, The Annie Tillery Mysteries and The Buccaneer Series. She produces and hosts a local access TV show for authors, The Writer's Dream, and lectures on topics in forensic science.

www.lindamariafrank.com

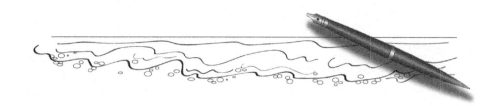

LARRY'S WARS

by

Joel W. Harris

CHAPTER ONE

A friendly get-together was planned for that
afternoon. What in fraternity talk was called a "smoker,"
between our super liberal Jewish guys and the only Black
frat on campus. That my college career, on life support for
my sophomore year, was about to die did not keep me,
Larry Levine, from helping Sam Johnson, one of my
buddies from the other group, to set up the room a few
hours in advance.

While we placed tables, chairs, glassware and snacks
my mind was locked on my only hope to stay enrolled, an
appointment that same afternoon with the Dean of
Students. A brief and desperate correspondence had
succeeded in getting me an in-person opportunity to
explain my apparent lack of scholarship and egregious

misbehavior, and to ask for a chance to move forward on a promise of reform and good behavior.

In the meantime, there was work to be done. But Sam was curious.

"I hear your days here are numbered." He said. "How did you go so wrong?

"You have time for my sad story? Could be long. Could be dull, too."

"Let's hear it. I'll be the judge."

"Soon as I arrived, I got involved with Campus Life, our bimonthly. Totally absorbed. I was in their office all day, sometimes. Neglected my schoolwork. So, two things happened at the end of my freshman year. First the graduating editor-in-chief rewarded my efforts and made me his successor."

"An honor most intelligent people would avoid."

"Right. But it's what I wanted. Then my joy was cut short two days later, when I got put on probation.

"Another honor most intelligent people would avoid."

"Right again. And the second year was worse. My grades were falling along with circulation, sales too low to pay the printer. Playboy had just hit the stands and was stealing my readers. I tried cute stuff, like the Sex Life of the Female Rice Krispie: *Sexus vita feminae rice crispie.* Swimming in milk, snap is the mating call, crackle is the climax and pop is the results."

"Too racy for the dean?"

"How was I to know? And then I ran the essay on the follies of sesquipedalia. He liked that one, but it didn't sell magazines, so I tried to copy Playboy's style."

"You got out some great issues."

"That the Dean called pedaling porn on campus, thank you. And between my grades, what he officially termed inappropriate content, and sticking the school with our printing bills I was told not to bother registering for my junior year."

"So, you're out?'

"Probably. I have one last chance to plead my case. I'm seeing the Dean in about ten minutes. That's why I'm wearing a jacket and tie. Need to look serious, businesslike, mature."

"You could almost fool me."

My story was interrupted by the delivery of the keg of beer we had ordered.

"Thirsty?" I asked.

"I'll pass on it for now. Maybe later."

I had seen kegs of beer before but was never in charge of one. Tapping it always looked like a simple task. Position the syphon/faucet over the bung and push down, which is what I did.

"Larry," Sam said. "Not so fast."

But it was too late. A gusher out of the keg, around the hardware, landed on my jacket, shirt and tie. Now all soaked with beer.

"You have to screw down the syphon first." Sam said.

"Now you tell me? Thanks for the instructions. I'll remember for next time."

"You're dripping beer. You can't see the dean like that. I'll explain what happened."

"And make things worse."

"Don't I know it. What do I do now?"

"I'll lend you, my shirt. At least it's dry."

"And has a tribal motif."

"Part of my cultural heritage. You have a problem with that?"

"We can discuss that later. Hand it over."

So, he gave me the shirt off his back. How's that for friendship?

Standing in front of the dean's desk, waiting. I have yet to say a word. He looks at me, up and down in silence, then at the papers on his desk, then back at me. Finally, he spoke.

"Mr. Levine, we have nothing to talk about. Let me know when you grow up."

Had he made up his mind in advance? Or is it possible that wearing a dashiki to our conference was not such a good idea?

Either way, I now had two things to do, both necessary and dreaded. I had to tell my parents, and I had to find a job, at least until my future arrived. That future was no mystery.

The Korean unpleasantness was continuing, and without my student deferment I was destined to be drafted.

About the Author
Joel W. Harris

Born and raised in Brooklyn and living in Woodmere for the last 58 years with my beautiful wife, Evvy. Retired from a career in insurance spanning over 60 years I continue to be an avid reader as well as a writer and have over 3,000 books in my home library.

FINDING RAYNE

by

Lisa Jagmohan

Life takes on a whole new meaning when you're an adult. I couldn't have asked for a better life in the most wonderful city. I travel the world. I have a successful, rapidly expanding career. I am the fittest I have ever been. It's all about me and what I want to do, when I want to do it. The mentality I had to embrace at an early age to put myself first and go after what has always mattered the most, Rayne. I can't be anything to anyone else until I know who I am. Living in New York has taught me many things; the main lesson is that you can have it if you want it. You can live that dream; you can be in that dream and have it just as you want it.

I am Rayne Luna, CEO and COO of a company I built with my own two hands, all stemming from the notion that I could be whatever I wanted to be. Dad wanted me in finance, like him, to follow in his footstep. Mom just wanted me to be happy. She always said, you can make any passion into a career, you can be as successful as you choose to be, but you have to be passionate about it, and that's what mattered the most. My life should be full of passion, passion for the work that I did, passion for the people that I came across and passion for life in general. This way I would take it all in and every single moment would matter. I combined my love for seeing people, being around people, seeing people smile with the desire to make money at doing something I truly enjoyed. I created the very successful 'Luna Nova', a venue like no other venue, Top of the line staging, multi floor accommodations, fully functional event venue. The birth of Luna Nova was created with a combination of my passion for creating things, my attention to detail and simply my love of happy places. My love of combining different ethnicities and themes, to make that one moment unforgettable. Luna House now consists of four successful locations. I handle everything from A to Z. This way my talented event planners can share my vision and help bring that vision to life without handling the tedious issues.

There are days that I go to sleep exhausted, numbers crunching in my head, dreaming of ways to do things bigger and better than the last time. I still find the time to make time for mom and dad and my large family. There is barely any time for much more than that. I am happy with the way my life is heading and I wouldn't change a thing about it.

My small suitcase is packed and ready to head to Pasadena, to finalize the deal for my fifth location. I fell in love with the area the moment I went to visit my best friend Rachel in the days before her wedding.

I walk up to a warmly decorated building that doesn't feel like an office, but more like a home; welcoming and happy, causing a smile to instantly form on my face. I am greeted by the warm glow of the receptionist. This is what life is all about. Warmth and cheeriness manifesting from one person to another without even speaking a word. This is the way I want people to feel when they walk into one of my establishments.

"Mr. Mykel Evans will see you now, please follow me."

"Hello, Miss Luna, glad to finally meet you. We have all the details ready to go over with you, I take it your trip here was a smooth one, and you are ready to get started."

For the first time in what feels like forever, I am lost for words. Standing before me is the most handsome man I have ever laid eyes on. Focus Rayne, focus. I tell myself and take a deep breath as I reply, carefully forming my words.

"Thank you for fitting me into your busy schedule, I

49

am glad this day has finally come; it's been a long, hard, road to get here, I hope you can help make this all as painless as possible."

He smiles at me, and his smile is softer and even warmer than his first. The hint of his accent makes me wonder where he originated from. I listen to the words roll off his tongue like honey and hang on to every word. I have to remind myself a few more times to focus but to also take it all in, because when I head back home, who knows if I will ever meet anyone like this again. Luna Nova is my focus today; that is what's important today, tomorrow and every day after that. I don't believe in love. I believe in success. I believe in passion, but love, not so much.

The next few months fly by in a flash. I throw myself into getting the new Luna up to mark as the others. I have days that blend into nights and in no time, I lose track of time and the months that fly by.

"You need to take a break, Rayne." My grandmother says to me. Her advice has always been what I listen to first. I close my eyes and still hear her voice in my head. "You may think you have it all, but one little thing is missing. The one little thing, most of us are lucky to have in our lifetime. Don't let the time and the opportunity pass you by, Rayne. He's the one." I turn and close my eyes, because right now I am too tired to hear what she is saying, and too tired to think of anything more or even make sense of it.

My new location is bigger and better than the rest. I walk in the door early in the morning and could not be happier with the way that it turned out. I know it's not wise, but I mentally pat myself on the back. The holidays are coming, and I will be ready for the new flow of customers ready to experience the new Luna Nova.

As I decorate my tree and fully deck out my house with silver and red decorations, I turn slowly as I can feel a presence in the room with me.

"Rayne, my dear..."

"Grandma, you have to stop popping up like this, you're going to give me a heart attack one day..."

She laughs and gives me that devious look she always has. "Rayne, my dear, Christmas was always my favorite, always took pride in my decorating, I am happy to know that you take after me in that way, your mother not so much."

"Of course, grams, I wouldn't have it any other way. I am glad that you can share all of this with me. How does it look?" She smiles, her eyes showing her approval. It could look like crap, and she would still approve. That's just the amazing person that she is.

"Looks good. One day you will have someone else to share it with, and you won't need me anymore; then I can rest and not worry about you so much."

"Grandma, I am fine, there is no need to worry, I am happy with the way my life is, I am happy that it's just me, I am so busy I can't even have a dog, because I wouldn't have time for it. I am happy, I really am. You do not need to worry about me."

And then, just like that, she disappears. I smile because the absolute best part of my life has always been having Grams around. It feels like she is always there, and when I need her the most, she somehow knows. So, yes, I count myself extremely blessed.

The holidays come and go. Between the renovations in my house and the constant visits from Grandma, I have to finagle my schedule to squeeze in time for Mom and Dad. They called last week to say they are coming in this week for a visit. Of course, I have to set some time aside to spend with them and do something fun. I am almost done with getting the guest room ready, nothing but the best for them, the people that created me.

"Give your mother my love, Rayne, I miss her, more than you will ever know..."

"I'm sure she misses you too, Gramms; stay, even for a little, just so you can see them."

"I don't want to complicate things and make them worse. He will call you; answer when he calls, Rayne, some things are just meant to be..."

"Grandma, what are you talking...." I spin around and again, she is gone. Why does she do that? Who's going to call me? Wishful thinking, I guess. I shrug it off, labelling her an exhausted, over-thinking, grandma while I continue readying my space.

We head out to make our dinner reservation in time, I I'm never late, no matter where I am or what I am doing. My schedule is what keeps me focused and I cannot have it any other way.

"It's so good to see you Rayne; we miss you so much. It's' good to see that you're looking good, despite your busy, overloaded life. You need to slow down."

"Mom, I am doing well; you worry too much. You, though, are looking tired and drained. What's been going on with you?"

"She does nothing but worry all the time; that's why she needed to come visit; she needs to see for herself that you are doing ok. You're a big girl and we know you can handle yourself, but you're just so far, and we don't even see you enough." Dad jumps in, his eyes dancing as he looks at me.

"I know, soon enough, I will have more time on my hands, and you will be tired of seeing me. I will be in Miami all the time."

We all smile, because they think that would never happen, and I know I can definitely be a pain when the time is right.

"Rayne, is that you...." I turn at the sound of my name spoken by a voice that sounds so familiar. I take in the glorious sight of Mykel Evans walking toward our table.

"Hi, how are you, good to see you. What are you doing in this neck of the woods?"

"Visiting my mom here, for a few days. Good to see you; how is everything going with Luna?"

"You remembered the name?"

"Yea, kind of hard to forget." That smile again; somehow, I didn't forget it

"It's going well, thank you again for all your help. I couldn't have done this without you."

"How about you jot down your number and we can talk more, if you don't mind. I don't want to interrupt your dinner any more than I already have."

I introduce him to my parents and save my number in his phone. I give him one last smile, as he returns the smile and melts my heart both at the same time. The moment he takes the bag packed with, what I assume to be his dinner, from the waitress, he turns and looks my way, and smiles again. This time, he lingers there, his eyes holding mine. Then he turns and walks out; I don't move my eyes from that direction until a few minutes after he disappears. I watch him until I can no longer see him disappear out of the restaurant. I compose myself and look to see Mom and Dad looking at me with somewhat of a smirk on their face, quiet, almost smiling, not saying a word. Somehow, I know exactly what they are thinking.

"So....he's handsome."

"Mom, please, he's just a business associate; I almost forgot his name there for a moment.

"...But then you remembered...." Mom's warm smile brightens her entire face. I leave the conversation there because that glow on her face is what I enjoy seeing the most, so I just take it all in.

I have some great new ideas to add to my inventory at Luna. I know quickly expanding is not such a good idea but it's happening. The New Luna has taken off like a fighter jet. Business is as busy as ever and the constant flow has my head spinning with the never-ending need to make it bigger and better.

"Hey Grandma." I see her appear beside me before she even says a word to me. "I missed you for a few days, where were you? Why didn't you come see me?"

"I didn't want to open that can of worms just yet, Rayne. Your mom doesn't understand a lot of things and she is just set in her old ways."

"Whatever it is, she's your daughter and she misses you just as much as I do, she just wants to know that you're ok, and my telling her you're ok is much different than knowing for herself."

"That's stressful for us all, I don't want her to feel the pain all over again. We were close and this killed her. It was my fault. She didn't handle it well. I watched her break over and over again. She fell apart day by day and you also, of course."

"Grams..."

"He's going to call you; be on your best behavior, Rayne. Let him see the true person that you are, kind, sincere, loving, artistic, smart in every way. He's the one, Rayne, I see it. He is meant for you. That day you met him; he wasn't even supposed to be there. It was fate. You have finally found the person to ft your soul. Don't say anything; just listen to me. Once in a lifetime, if you are lucky, you find love. Real love. Love that doesn't make you question life or love in any way. It's a constant smooth flow, that no matter how much you fight, it won't go away. That's rare, Rayne. Some people never find love. There is no greater purpose in life than that experience. Take it from me. I have waited for this moment for a long time, Rayne, and, yes, I know you can take care of yourself, but I will finally be able to rest knowing there is someone there beside you to help you and take care of you if the need arises. Someone that can share in the same joys and interests as you, someone to complete you. Someone that will love you, almost as much as I do."

"I have you, Grams. I don't need anything or anyone else." I mean that with every inch of my soul. Other people only complicate things, partners, husbands, wives. It's so simple just being by myself. I have no time to give to anyone else. Luna Nova takes all my time.

"I can't be here forever, Rayne. I can finally rest; this is the only reason I have been hanging around. It's not wise for an old woman like me to cramp your style and be here all the time. Answer the phone, Rayne. He will call."

"Who's going to call?"

"Mykel" she whispers. I feel her lips brush my forehead just for a second, wondering if I heard her right or I'm just imagining things.

"Grams, how did you know about...." My head shoots up and she's gone. I hate when she does that; she just disappears and I'm sure she knows it drives me crazy, but she does it anyway, over and over again.

I can't wait to hit my bed tonight. It's been such a long day. I run out of the shower as I hear my phone ringing on my nightstand. I answer without even looking at the screen, water dripping everywhere.

"Rayne, I hope I didn't catch you at a bad time. I just wanted to touch base with you." I stand still for a moment taking in the voice. That voice that has become familiar even though I've only heard it a few times. That voice that feels like it's a part of me already, like it completes my day. The voice that seems so familiar, like I have heard it a million times before.

"Hi, Mykel, not a bad time at all." I answer without thinking.

"It was good seeing you...I've been thinking about you since you left my office and there you were, in my old hometown."

That's when it hits me. How the hell did she know he was going to call me. This is so crazy I want to laugh but realize, he's going to think I'm crazy if I laugh. I have enough secrets as it is. Grams said he's going to call, that he's the one. It's crazy that I am even connecting the two

58

things, but here he is on the other line, waiting for me to reply, ... just as Grams said.

"It was good seeing you, too...."

For Rayne's full story, look for 'Finding Rayne'

Lisa Jagmohan.com

About the Author
Lisa Jagmohan

Lisa Jagmohan, born in Queens, New York and moved to Long Island over ten years ago for a more quiet life. Lisa has 7 published books and is currently working on her 8th in a new series. She has received numerous awards and recognitions for her writings.

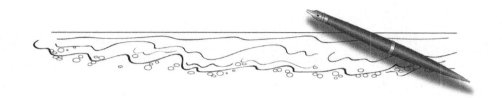

I REMEMBER:

BEAUTY COMES BACK

by

JoAnn Vergona Krapp

I REMEMBER the day Beauty walked back into our lives.

He had been part of a litter left in our backyard. Charles noticed the box first.

"There's four of them," he cried out. They were huddled together, eyes half-closed, mewing in unison. One by one, I lifted them out—snow white, smoky gray, tiger striped, and black spotted.

"We keep them, right?" my brother's six-year-old mind reasoned. Four years older, I knew better.

So did Mother. "One!"

We picked Snow White. When Daddy put the others into the car, he promised, "I'll fInd them a new home."

Snow White was our darling for three weeks. The novelty of a first pet and the onset of summer ...perfect... until... one morning we found her stretched out on the back porch, stone still.

"Her neck is broken," Daddy said, "probably another cat. I heard the noise last night."

We buried her in the empty lot nearby. Sitting on the front steps some two weeks later, we noticed a small gray creature walking up the block. I squinted, "No...couldn't be." It continued with deliberation, reached our house, stopped, sat up and stared. Charles bounded down the steps and crouched beside it. "He came back," he whispered. In a hushed tone, he decided, "It's a sign...we have to keep him."

And we did. We named him Gray Beauty.

Like Snow White, he lived outdoors, making his home under the backyard steps. Once we coaxed him inside. He got as far as the dining room, splayed out his legs, straightened up, and scrambled outside.

Time saw Beauty grow into a full-sized feline, independent and loyal. He developed a routine. At 5:00 AM, Monday through Friday, he escorted our father, a mailman, across the street to the bus stop. At 8 AM, he accompanied Charles and me down the street to PS 176.

He was a quiet cat, demanding little attention, content to follow us around the yard and watch us play. So, it went for three years.

"We're moving to Valley Stream," Mother announced. We'll have to leave Beauty here. Cats don't take much to new locations."

Protesting did no good. My cousins moved in the day we moved out and promised they'd take care of Beauty. We left him November 8, 1952.

Two weeks later, on our fIrst visit back to Brooklyn, we dashed to the back stairs and whistled for him.

Nothing.

"He's gone," my cousin said. "He disappeared after you left. I'm really sorry."

Our parents offered us another cat. Too soon. Charles and I needed to feel the presence of Beauty a while longer.

One afternoon, Charles' friend Billy rang our doorbell and breathlessly declared, "I saw a gray cat roaming around. Maybe it's Beauty!"

We searched...and searched. If it was, Charles and I never saw Beauty again.

In the years to follow, we had other cats. But it's the memory of the first one that lingers on.

About the Author
JoAnn Vergona Krapp

JoAnn Vergona Krapp is a library media specialist whose articles on children's literature have appeared in numerous library journals In addition to writing, Ms. Krapp is a watercolor artist. She works and resides in Farmingdale, Long Island, where she teaches writing and painting workshops for children. She is a member of the national and regional Society of Children's Writers and Illustrators and the Islip Arts Council. Her books and paintings can be viewed at www.JVKArts.com.

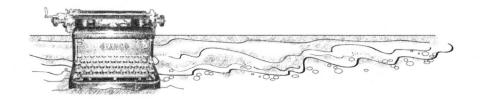

THE WORST HANUKKAH EVER

by

Sandy Lanton

The snow crunched under Rachel's feet as she left the hospital with her family.

"Why did Grandpa have to break his hip now?" complained Rachel.

"He'll be home soon," said her mother. "You'll be able to spend plenty of time with him while he recovers from his surgery."

"But Hanukkah starts in two days and lasts for only eight days. Grandpa won't be home 'til it's all over. It will be the worst Hanukkah ever," said Rachel.

"We'll still light the candles," said her mother. "We'll still sing Hanukkah songs," said her father. "We'll still play dreidel," said her brother, David.

"I'll still make potato latkes," said Grandma.

"Without Grandpa," insisted Rachel. "It will be the

worst Hanukkah ever."

"Grandpa tells us about the brave Macabee soldiers. He spreads his arms when he talks about the temple destroyed by the Syrians. He whispers when he speaks of the holy oil the Jews found to light the Menorah--enough to last only one day. He raises his eyes to Heaven when he speaks of the miracle- that the oil burned for eight days. His eyebrows rise when he announces that's why we celebrate Hanukkah, the Festival of Lights, for eight days and nights, light eight candles on the Menorah and eat potato pancakes and other foods cooked with oil. Grandpa says we play with dreidels because the letters spell out 'a great miracle happened there'." Rachel stopped to catch her breath.

"Even if all my aunts, uncles and cousins come over to light candles, sing songs, eat potato pancakes and play dreidel, Hanukkah isn't Hanukkah without everybody gathered around Grandpa while he recounts the tale."

The next day, the family bustled about preparing for Hanukkah. Rachel's mother, in the dining room, polished the Menorah.

Rachel whispered in her mother's ear. Her mother nodded. Rachel's father, in the living room, dusted off the song books. Rachel whispered something to her father. He smiled and picked up the telephone. David sat cross-legged in the family room, spinning his dreidel. Rachel spoke to her brother. He stopped spinning his dreidel and gathered up the pennies he used as the bank. Grandma, in the kitchen, fried potato pancakes. Rachel peeled potatoes and whispered to her grandmother. Grandma smiled for the first time since Grandpa's accident.

So, on the first night of Hanukkah, the whole family gathered in the dining room. At the head of the table sat the family's computer. On the screen was Grandpa's smiling face. Around him were doctors, nurses, and other patients. They all sang "Oh Hanukkah, Oh Hanukkah, "Who Can Retell," Rock of Ages," and "The Dreidel Song." Everyone said the prayers as they lit the Menorah. David and his cousins played dreidel. The family eagerly devoured Grandma's potato latkes. And everyone gathered around the computer while Grandpa recounted the story of Hanukkah. He never told it better.

"This is the best Hanukkah ever," thought Rachel.

About the Author
Sandy Lanton

Sandy Lanton, graduate of Queens College, majoring in psychology and early childhood education, turned her talents to writing. Her books: *Daddy's Chair, Lots of Latkes, Still a Family: A Yound Child's Story About Divorce, The Littlest Levine, The Happy Hackers*, and soon to be published, *Lilly Blue Riding Hood*. She appears in Appleseeds, Hopscotch, and Junior Scholastic as well as several anthologies.

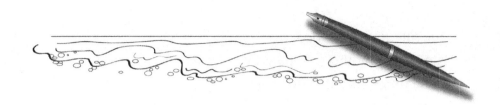

666 PINE ISLAND PLACE

by

Caryn M. McGill

I didn't always look like hell. Once, I stood three stories tall crowned with a cupola and a wind vane perpetually pointing north. Wrought iron curly cues, like the letter L written in ornate script, pinned my black shutters tightly to the gray clapboard. My paint gleamed, my wainscoting appeared dent-and-scratch-free, my twenty-foot ceilings embossed with glorious white federal molding. Rather than the current inhabitants of creepy crawly creatures, pesky feral animals, and ghoulish spirits, happy families lived here...for nearly two hundred years. I protected them from the elements with my sturdy roof and walls, and from the frigid temperatures with my toasty-warm fires.

I watched with a sense of immense satisfaction as fathers tickled their children to near hysteria before finally tucking them into bed, then reading a favorite bedtime story, and mothers prepared sumptuous family dinners, sometimes with the aid of a kitchen staff. Holidays were magnificent with grand Christmas trees and mountains of festively wrapped presents; the sweet smells of holiday treats permeating the air as they baked in my professional-grade oven. Music and song filled my hallways. Dancing feet pranced on my marble floors and people made love in my bedrooms, sweet, thrilling love. I tried not to watch, but sometimes I just couldn't help myself.

I felt like a worthy house, solid, set on a good foundation, hugged by magnificent magnolia trees and protected by sturdy oaks. Until the Sinclairs moved in...then everything went to shit. Perhaps if I'd been more patient, or just ignored them, I might have survived.

The moment they stepped across the threshold of my magnificent mahogany door with the stained glass window spelling out WELCOME, a chill spread through me. No matter how high I turned up the thermostat I still couldn't banish the dreadful iciness that penetrated my rafters. I shuddered, and the sound unnerved me...a sound I'd never made before.

The year was 1979. Dr. Sinclair, an eminent physician from New York, had just taken over old Doc Jensen's practice who'd recently succumbed to liver cancer attributed to years of excessive alcohol consumption. Honestly, the stories I'd overheard from the previous owners made me think the new doc was sorely needed.

Upon her arrival, Mrs. Sinclair's tall thin frame—her posture indicative of the stick up her ass—paraded around the first floor like a solider marching to war, her sharp spikey heels digging into my polished hardwood. I winced, and the wallpaper in my foyer wrinkled. My vents hissed, all the air seemed to get sucked out of me and I threw a few windows open so I could breathe. Nobody noticed.

Two children ran up the stairs, yelling and jumping around, as children are prone to do. But they didn't seem joyful, their screams more like shrieks, unsettling, evil. I didn't think there was such a thing as an innately evil child, but the second I saw them I knew this would turn out bad. Really bad. A few tears formed, the tiny droplets leaking from my faucets onto the ceramic basins with a bit of a plopping noise.

I tried to shove my anxiety and apprehension into my attic, giving myself a pep talk. *You're overreacting. You've been spoiled with wonderful loving families and these people are, well, just a little different. A little off... but everything will be okay after they settle in.* It always takes me a while to get used to new residents. Perhaps I'm still too old-fashioned. People are more sophisticated these days.

They smoke pot and believe in free love. I need to relax, chill out. Give them a chance.

Well, that attitude only lasted a goddamned week. I valiantly tried to ignore the giant gashes in my woodwork made by flying objects that should never become airborne. I really did. Mrs. Sinclair had a violent temper and both her children and her husband sported enough cuts and bruises to have her taken into custody. I couldn't comprehend why they put up with her abuse. I mean...her husband is a doctor for Christ's sake. He should know better. But Dr. Sinclair rarely made it home, spending long nights at his practice or the hospital and turned a blind eye to the dysfunctions of his family.

I witnessed the evilness of the children as they tortured small animals and also each other. A gleeful sneer would overtake their faces as they smeared their hands in the greasy red blood of their victims—painting their faces like war paint—and popped eyeballs with their feet. At times I couldn't decide who was more malicious, the kids or the mother. Often I felt the urge to scream and I did so. My wailing sounded like the wind mostly, and frequently resulted in comments like "This old house sucks." or "I hate this creepy house." I should have been angry at the insults, but instead I was...well...hurt.

The basement became my own personal hell. Dr. and Mrs. Sinclair never went down there, but the children made it into kind of a Dr. Frankenstein's laboratory. The smells alone nearly suffocated me. The rotting bodies of furry creatures littered the cement floor when they should have been out running through the dewy green grass in my yard. I have a magnifIcent yard hugging me; one where lovely flowers grow and people could sit and sip a cocktail on a hot summer evening.

About a month after the move-in date I decided I couldn't put up with one more second of this depravity. This repugnant family had to go.

That night the kids were watching a program on TV about a house that had apparently been overtaken by ghosts — who then murdered the entire family—a haunted house. Hmm...that sounded like something I might be able to pull off. Of course, I had no intention of murdering anyone, but if I stepped up my activities a bit perhaps I could scare them away. So far, my subtle overtures expressing my unhappiness: overturning chairs, giving a little push as they ran down the stairs, and hiding or breaking some of their treasured objects, went unnoticed, which only served to annoy me even further. It took a great mustering of energy to accomplish these small feats, something I was new at and admittedly not all that good at either. I was profIcient at opening and slamming shut doors and windows, but it took over an hour to muster enough force to lift an object off the ground or open a single drawer. I groaned and creaked with the effort, but then I realized this only added to my haunting. I smiled and the lights suddenly flashed brightly. Another fItting after-effect. Perfect.

I had to come up with something spectacular. Something that would scare the ever living shit out of them, and they'd flee without even packing a bag. I'd be left in peace, a new family would move in and all would be well again.

The whisper came in the night, just as the grandfather clock in my living room struck midnight. Initially I thought it might be Mrs. Sinclair, but she didn't know me, she never spoke to me. This voice sounded familiar. A woman I knew. I pitched my ears (which just happen to be everywhere) in the direction of the voice. "I'm here to help," she said. I peered into the darkness. The image of a slender body came into view. She sat on the olive green couch, legs crossed at the ankles, arms spread across the top of the sofa. Her white dress revealed a serious amount of cleavage and the skirt, enhanced with copious layers of crinoline, appeared tattered and torn. The distorted features of her face: nose pushed to one side, an eye swollen shut, a deep gash marring her forehead, crusted blood adorning the crown of her head— gave a garish facade in the faintness of the pale moonlight. *Elizabeth.*

The night her chauffeured limousine plunged off the cliff at the end of Gull Road is one I'll never forget. It was her debutante coming-out party, but she never made it to the ball. Tragedy never hit home so hard before, and the night turned into a horror fest of wailing and thrashing, a deep sadness I'd never experienced. I wept that night for the first time.

"Elizabeth," I whispered in the darkness. "Is it really you?"

"Yes." Her arms slipped off the sofa and her hands landed in her lap. Two fingers were missing. I groaned.

"Are you okay?" I tried to recall her former beauty: blonde ringlets that reflected the brilliant morning sunshine, clear blue eyes that took your breath away. *My beautiful Elizabeth.*

"I've been better, you?" Elizabeth stood and began to pace, her ethereal feet silent on the parquet floor.

"Well, I guess if you're here then you know I'm not doing well at all."

"I should say so," she assured me.

"How did you know?"

She stopped and peered out the window overlooking my garden of purple peonies. In the darkness they seemed more black than purple. "I used to love this garden," she said wistfully. My heart filled with the sadness of the memory of her sudden death and a puff of ash escaped from the hearth in the great room. The embers ignited.

"I do stop by now and again." The fingers on her good hand traced the square wooden frame of the windowpane. She pressed her bloated lips against the glass, her kiss cold.

"I never saw you," I confessed.

"I didn't want you to. I was jealous most of the time. Watching another girl sleep in my room, dancing where I used to dance. Remembering everything that was taken from me haunts me."

I groaned again, this time too loudly. My faucets leaked copiously.

"But I love you," she said, still facing my window. "Every day I spent with you was wonderful. I want you to know I appreciated you. I admired your majestic beauty, the comforts you gave me. I miss you."

Heat rose around me and I heard the thermostat click on. I loved Elizabeth too. I wished she'd lived a long life. A life here. With me.

Elizabeth floated toward the couch, perching herself on the edge of the middle cushion, her hands folded primly on her lap again, the stolen fingers less obvious. "I've been watching, but it seems like you can't do this alone," she said.

I smiled and the shutters guarding the living room windows broke free, flapping enthusiastically like an audience at a rock concert. A real ghost? Reinforcements? Just what I needed. Relief comforted me like the nights when the fireplaces were all lit and the golden glow of burning coals blanketed me in warmth.

"I can use some help," I muttered. "I've been making my best effort but mostly these wretched people just ignore me or insult me. They're certainly not noticing my unhappiness."

She sighed, a loud whooshing sound. "If you're going for a haunting, you're doing a terrible job. An occasional push down the stairs, hiding or breaking things? Blinking lights, creaky noises? You call that a plan?"

Elizabeth was right, my attempt a pathetic endeavor. "Obviously, I don't really know what I'm doing."

"The first problem is you're being too nice. These are dreadful people. You're going to have to step it up if you want to intimidate them enough to leave."

83

Nice? I didn't think I was being nice at all. Maybe she was right. I needed her help. I was desperate. "Okay," I said.

"We need to get to work then. I've got some ideas."

It took nearly a week to formulate our plan and Elizabeth proved to be invaluable. She became a malevolent force that morphed into different forms and would slap, grope, threaten or otherwise freak the hell out of the children. She only pestered them, never showing herself, and when they complained to their parents they were shrugged off as just seeking attention. The stage was set.

We checked the weather and scheduled our fright night for the impending storm on Friday. It wasn't Friday the thirteenth, regrettably. That would have been awesome! The children slept soundly in their beds that night, dreaming their awful nightmares that only gave them more ghoulish ideas for torturing innocents. In my estimation it would soon include young humans, as the children seemed to be getting bored with the usual furry creatures that unwittingly wandered the grounds before being snatched and flayed alive. I shuddered at the horrid thoughts of what might come and my walls creaked violently. I was getting stronger, more focused. Elizabeth and I had been working during the hours when the family wasn't home. She taught me how to use my anger to fire up the energy I needed to get things done. I practiced and practiced and finally we were ready. I was ready.

The wind howled. The branches of my protectors snapped against my windowpanes. They knew what I was up to and waved encouragement. Flashes of lightning sparked the air with errant energy and I scooped it up and ignited the wires in my walls. Heat began to melt the paint and it slid down in gooey rivulets of bubbly white ooze.

Elizabeth faced me in the giant mirror over the living room fireplace, her swollen lips stretching into an eerie grin. "This is going to be fun!" she exclaimed, clapping her hands together like she did as a child and her father brought home something pretty from his business trip.

Lightning crackled, illuminating the blue-black sky, and the sound waves of thunder skittered across the night air. The mighty oaks voiced their encouragement, swaying back and forth, slapping their leaved fingers against my windowpanes, and howling their approval. The excitement energized me, what I imagine adrenaline would feel like. I felt so alive, so in control, so...*deliciously evil.*

Elizabeth entered the daughter's room first. She railed, screeching a ghoulish shriek and the girl awoke, bolting upright. My wraithlike partner-in-crime few around the bedroom, darting up to the ceiling then through the wall and back in again. The child ran to the door but I slammed it in her face and turned the lock. Trapped. Elizabeth grabbed her and hurled her back onto the bed. "You evil little devil," she screamed. "You're a monster. You don't deserve this house. You must die!"

The girl peed her bed and the intensity of the encounter emboldened me. I recalled the terrible events of the last few weeks and convinced myself the kid was getting what she deserved. "Mommy! Mommy! Help!" she yelled. But the thunder drowned out her pathetic cries for salvation. She clawed at my door, her fingernails etching deep scratches in my beautiful wood, then fainted, her unconscious form slumped against the locked door. I smiled.

We moved to the next room.

Elizabeth's powers awed me. My walls oozed red blood. Black puffs of smoke flew from her hands, forming hideous creatures with sharp fangs and claws that threatened to tear the flesh off the human form. She became a dervish of dark energy as she whirled through the son's room in similar fashion, tying him to the bed with the bungee cords he used to restrain his own victims. His screams eventually pierced through the rumble of thunder and the cracks of lightning, awakening the good doctor and his wife.

I should have at least saved him. He might have had a better life if the remainder of his insidiously evil family had finally left him to do the wonderful work he performed on a daily basis.

A violent streak of lightning struck the weather vane but I was too old for a lightning rod. The attic burst into fames and licks of fire danced down my grand staircase. Elizabeth, in her maniacal glee, blew on the flames and it was as if she'd just poured gasoline on them. An inferno of hell-fire spread across my floors, my halls filled with smoke. I couldn't breathe. "Elizabeth!" I yelled. "Stop! You're killing me!" I hadn't intended for it to go this far. I just wanted to scare the bejeezus out of them and get them the hell out of here. I quickly unlocked the doors, one after the other, but it was too late. The fire too intense, the smoke too thick. If I had a sprinkler system I would have turned it on. I burst my pipes hoping that would quell the fames, but no luck. Not in time to save them. The flesh burned off their bones. I retched and heaved, my beams shuddering in great sighs of anguish at what I'd done.

I searched for Elizabeth but she'd vanished. I wondered where she'd gone and if maybe this was her calling. Unleashing her anger and regrets wherever they are needed. The thought saddened me further. Such a beautiful and loving child relegated to a miserable existence in the afterlife. Whatever the hell that meant.

I was alone and on fire. I felt no pain, only sadness, and an overwhelming sense of impending emptiness.

And now...

I'm just a burned-out hull. My charred beams barely support the upper floors. My shutters lean haphazardly left or right, some torn from my sides completely. Most of my skin has crumbled, only a few boards of siding still attached and unscathed. Not much glass remains, allowing any creature access through my broken windows. There's bird crap everywhere. I'm just a skeleton of what used to be a magnificent dwelling filled with loving people and beautiful accouterments. No one will ever come here again. Never will I smell the savory dishes being prepared in my kitchen, hear the laughter of children, or the sweet sounds of lovemaking in the master suite. For I have no kitchen, no attic, no living room or bedrooms. I am mostly a basement. Forced to live in the dirt, the ashes of what was once a proud existence.

Elizabeth and her friends sometimes hang out here. But there is no joy, no laughter, no dancing, just the malevolent presence of ghosts plotting their next fright night. It seems like I've become the training ground for evil souls new to their sordid deathly duties. A hellish extension of Satan's empire. Sometimes I think Elizabeth used me and that she wasn't here to help me at all. I don't talk to her any more, preferring to remember the lovely girl she was and not the evil demon she has become.

I have no tears left to shed, as my pipes are empty, no groans to make, as my walls have disintegrated, no hearths to light or heat to turn up to banish the perpetual chill. The whistling noise that blows through the remnants of my hallways isn't me anymore...it's just *the wind*.

I guess if people knew what I'd done they'd probably say I got what I deserved.

Maybe they'd be right. The worst part, however, is that the Sinclairs are still here and have joined Elizabeth's evil gang of demons. Not Dr. Sinclair, as he most likely moved on to a happier place—but the three evil ones, and if I thought they were evil before, well, I was wrong. Dead wrong.

About the Author
Caryn M. McGill

Caryn grew up on the beaches of Long Island's East End. When she's not writing, you can find her in the kitchen whipping up something scrumptious or in the studio, painting and fusing glass into decorative dishes. She writes paranormal under her legal name and romantic suspense as Kendra Greenwood.

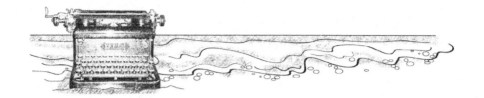

AT THE END OF MY ROPE

by

Michael O'Keefe

Piracy was my crime, and I would swing for it, a fitting end for a lucrative and violent career. How I got into this business was a bit more tangled; full of intrigue, world- hopping, and time travel. Though my punishment would be appropriate, I was a man out of time, existing beyond time's reckoning.

I was in the year of our Lord, 4529. Condemned to die, I was on the planet Aegina, in the Kepler solar system, to be hung by the neck by the Ministry of Justice of the Universal Democratic Monarchy. Yes, the universe has a king, and he doesn't like pirates. We were in Aegina's capital city of Casai Shima, but city is a misnomer. Aegina is comprised of 99.6 % water. The .4 % of land being small volcanic archipelagos and coral atolls. Casai Shima was where the Monarchy's forces caught up with me. So here is where I will hang.

Funny thing, a society that has perfected infinite ways to kill its sentient beings in an instant of unspeakable horror, it still chose to kill its pirates in the gruesome, old-fashioned way, just as it did on Earth since the first millennium. So, I would stretch at the end of a rope.

This wasn't the worst place to die. The gallows were situated on a bluff above Aegina's fine blue-sand beaches, overlooking the majestic Ochian Sea, where sea mammals swam and played. The large blood-orange Kepler sun was warm on my face, the hot rays cooled by soft sea breezes. The two-headed gulls' melodious calls as they flew about the coast were like lullabies, accompanied by the waves cascading against the shore. My reverie was broken by the tread of the executioner climbing the stairs, the footfalls softer and lighter than I would have imagined. The hangman in black cloak and hood came from behind. The sweet smell of cinnamon and currants wafting forward and washing over me.

******

I was just fourteen when the beguiling Desdemona Kelly convinced me to flee with her from my beloved home of Dunfanaghy, on the coast of Donegal. She was only fifteen herself and already bored with the life of a girl in an Irish fishing village. Being 1649, she had little means of escape. But my Desi was a clever girl, bordering on diabolical. Of course, she found a way.

An enchantress, Desi's long thick red hair bounced behind her in cadence with her graceful movements, catching the sun and demanding I be enthralled. I was, from the first day I saw her. She smelled of cinnamon and currants, like warm soda bread fresh from the kiln. Tall, lithe yet curvaceous, with emerald eyes that snatched the soul right out of me, I would do her bidding until the ending of my days, which upon this scaffold, today seemed to be.

Following her like a devoted puppy, we stowed away on a ketch bound for Liverpool, making our way by foot and the occasional stolen horse to London. There we signed on to the crew of a galiot bound for Nassau in the Caribbean. The captain, a disgraced Royal Naval officer, had difficulty attracting a reputable crew, so he more than welcomed us.

Captain Percy Trevor was a privateer, taking prizes on behalf of the Crown, with a handsome cut for himself and his crew. Until King Charles was assassinated, touching off the English Civil War. All pretense of government cover was lost to us, and with it any reservation or compunction. The Golden Age of piracy began in that vacuum of order, and Captain Trevor was the most voracious pirate of the age.

Desi and I learned our trade at the knee of the master. No longer consigning ourselves to taking prizes from enemies of the Crown—what with no one wearing it—we raided everything that floated in those tropical waters. Trevor thought us naturals at mayhem. In truth, Desi was the natural. I was only skilled at complying with whatever she suggested, no matter how outrageous. While this resulted in my hands being saturated with blood, the lust for it was all hers. For me, all of that slaughter felt more like a gift to my beloved than murder. We were so rapacious; Trevor designated the two of us as his trusted first mates.

This exhilarating and thriving existence might have continued, but for Captain Trevor's affinity for the harlots. Coupled with copious amounts of rum, while ashore, all he did was drink and rut. It wasn't long before the *syph* took its toll, robbing him of all of his wits and much of his vigor.

"Percy has gone mad from his whore-mongering," Desi said.

"In this life, laid and crazy might not be a bad way to go," I observed.

"True enough," she said. "But the captain's poor judgment will likely take us down as well." "What to do then, my love?"

"I think it's nigh-all time for a mutiny."

That is how Desdemona, and I became co-captains of the pirate ship Horrendous. Out of love for Desi and fear for myself, the crew fell in behind us. With her inspiration, I had become the most dreaded pirate on the seas, such a swath of murder and pillage had I cut. So, when I broached the subject of mutiny with the crew, I was met with nothing but fearful nods.

"The crew doesn't much speak to me," I said later to Desi.

"Because they're scared to death of you, Malachy." She laughed.

"Why would they be afraid of me?"

"You've killed more people than the bubonic plague."

"But that was work. Ordinarily, I'm a nice, easy-going *fella*."

"The crew doesn't think so. Did you know they called you *Black Malachy?*"

"They'd better call me Captain Black Malachy if they know what's good for 'em," I snarled.

We captained that ship for a few happy years, our lives enriched by bountiful helpings of rum, sodomy, and the lash. With no one to stop us, we were perfect scourges.

97

Merchant ships and men-o-war alike saw our Jolly Roger flying from our mast in their nightmares—until 1658. With the Crown restored and a new governor of Nassau appointed, the regime focused the full power of the Royal Navy on our heads. When not raiding ships at sea, we spent the majority of our time running for our lives.

Panic is the bedfellow of risk, and we took too many. We sought shelter in the waters north of Puerto Rico, in the section of the Atlantic called the Bermuda Triangle. We thought fear and superstition would keep our pursuers at bay. We also believed His Majesty's sailors wanted nothing to do with the raging storm into which we sailed. We were correct on both counts, but events soon justified the superstition. There was more in those waters than rough currents and bad weather. With our sails struck and hatches battened, we sought to ride out the storm below.

"Do you think the ship will hold?" Desi asked.

"Oh sure," I said, confident the Horrendous could survive anything of this world.

Beneath the waves was something not of this world at all. The Horrendous seemed to be snatched from the sea as if swallowed by a whale. We careened until the ship and all within it were suspended in thin air. We learned that this was just an effect of the enormous anti-gravity chamber within which we were trapped. The chamber was just one of many peculiar features of the colossal intergalactic pirate ship that snatched us up and few into space. Our reality was explained by Captain Ivan Ratchakokov, commander of the pirate spaceship Groaza. His English was a halting thing; his accent similar to Russian, which we had only heard once and briefly from one of our crew on the Horrendous. We weren't sure what the Russian was saying. So, we killed him.

"Dobro! You ship and crew now our prize," the Captain said.

"Where are you taking us?" Desi demanded.

"Where not right question," he grunted. "When is better one."

"Galaxies, you mean like other planets?" I asked. "Not just other planets. But *all* planets."

The Captain paused to let that register.

"What did you mean by *when?*" Desi asked.

"To go so far, so fast, need to cross time. Moving now at one thousand times speed of light, to planet Carmora in year 3415."

"What?" Desi and I said, our minds thoroughly blown.

Captain Ratchakokov waved us off.

"No time to waste explaining things primitive minds

99

can't understand. Right now, you have decision. Surrender and join us?"

"What if we don't?" Desi asked.

"Then you food for crew."

"You eat other people?" I asked, aghast.

"Technically, *people* is Earth term. Not many of crew from there. We actually whole other species—mostly same, but different. So, not cannibalism."

"It's still gross," Desi observed.

"Believe me," the captain snorted "Not many things in universe as savory as roast human. We discuss later—maybe not. For now, you join us for dinner, or you *be* dinner?"

In as much as we were in a futuristic spaceship, hurtling through time and the universe, we figured, what the hell? His awful English notwithstanding, Ratchakokov turned out to be a gracious host. He recognized our leadership qualities and welcomed us into his officer class. Our crew assimilated into the yeoman existence of the other space pirates.

The captain saw to our education as well. The science officer explained all of the technical marvels of the ship and the nuances of space-time navigation. The history officer taught us how to access the entire history of the universe throughout the whole of existence. No one could retain that much information, but we were trusted with the ship's vast computer system, so it was all at our fingertips. We now had the knowledge to travel anywhere in the universe, during any time—past, present, or future.

As I said, Ratchakokov was gracious, but naïve and a poor judge of character. He failed to detect Desi's ruthless ambition and my pathological need for bedlam. After two years honing our craft as intergalactic pirates, Desi and I staged our second mutiny.

After taking command of the Groaza, one of the adjustments we needed to make was in the manner of punishment. It was only a matter of time before some of the crew misbehaved. They were, after all, pirates. Captain Trevor had taught us back on the Horrendous, the first rule for maintaining obedience on a pirate ship was to communicate to the crew that malefactors would be dealt with severely. Of all the punishments in the pirate handbook, there was only one penalty—death. We were left to our imaginations as to how to affect that. As sea pirates, having someone walk the plank was a straightforward thing. You just marched them at sword point off the edge of the ship. In space at hyper-speed, that was a difficult proposition. Desi found an alternative.

"We'll just stuff him into the garbage chute and shoot

him into space," she suggested.

"Brilliant!" I agreed.

That was the last the ship ever saw of former Captain Ivan Ratchakokov.

As we spent the next four hundred years in real-time shuttling about the universe throughout the totality of existence, we discovered a few things. Some beneficial, like time travel halting the aging process. Desi and I were still in our mid-twenties four centuries later.

"Do you think we're immortal?" I asked.

"No," she said. "Ratchakokov surely died at our hands, and we lose a few men every raid. So, I think we can be killed. We just don't get older."

"Best we don't get careless then," I said.

Another happy discovery was that not only could we travel anywhere in the universe at any time, but we could return as many times as we saw fit. This was a good thing for the purse. The richest pirate prize ever taken in the whole breadth and history of the universe was the Urca de Lima, a Spanish galleon treasure ship taken and sunk off the coast of Florida, on planet Earth, in 1715. Gold being dearly valued everywhere in the universe, the gold lifted from that ship was worth more than two hundred million British Pounds in its contemporary time. The value in the present and future is priceless. Desi and I have taken it over one hundred times.

As time went on—ad infinitim—we received the inevitable challenges from disillusioned crew members who thought they were better suited to lead than Desi and meself. We thwarted every challenge, but the problem of the punishment serving as a deterrent for future attempted coups was a thorny one. In the old days on Earth, a simple keelhauling would suffice to dissuade further misguided ambitions. Witnessing the gory, painful, and slow death of a traitor being dragged across the barnacles on the bottom the ship, tearing them to shreds while simultaneously drowning would squelch even the most ambitious future treason. Keelhauling someone under a spaceship was an impractical matter, if not an impossibility. Desi, ever the creative one, hit on a solution.

"We'll find a planet with a craggy mountain range," she said. "Then we hover over the mountains and slowly drag the wretch until there's nothing left of him but his foot in the tractor beam."

"That would work," I nodded.

"Or," she said excitedly, "we'll find a planet with oceans that have sharks and sea monsters. We dangle the villain until just his head is above the water and wait for the sea beasties to have at him."

"That'll be enough, Desi," I said, wincing. "*Jaysus*, woman, but you scare me sometimes."

Thanks to Desdemona's diabolic planning and my swift and brutal execution, it would come as no surprise when we became the most feared pirates in universal history. But, in point of fact, only I did. Desi killed as many as I, but I got all the credit. Because she was a woman—and a beautiful one at that—no one believed she was capable of the carnage she committed. So, Captain Black Malachy O'Callaghan alone became the most wanted pirate in the universe. The fair Desdemona Kelly was believed to be my prisoner. If I weren't already the most sought-after fugitive in all of creation, imagine the innumerable conscripts attracted to the cause of a helpless damsel needing rescue from a cutthroat scoundrel like *meself*. It seems sexism isn't just timeless; it's eternal. What *bollocks*!

Our attempts to evade capture by the Crown Forces are what brought us to Casai Shima. Hoping to enjoy our spoils in a brief respite from raiding, Desi and I were holed up in a seaside bungalow. Lost in the throes of our unquenchable desire, the King's men came bursting through the door. They snatched me up in my altogether and thrashed me properly. Strangely, they set not a finger on Desi.

"Is this the infamous pirate, Malachy O'Callaghan?" the Crown's captain asked her.

She nodded, pulling the bedclothes tighter around her.

"You're a prisoner no more, Madam. You are safe now."

"Thank you," Desi said, weeping. "You can't imagine the hell of it all."

I couldn't believe she had betrayed me. She had picked this destination. Did she do so knowing the Crown's forces would be lying in wait for me? Had she arranged for them to be here? As bitter as the idea was, I bought into it. Upon interrogation, I lied and said she had always been my prisoner. I copped to every one of our shared crimes, exonerating her for all of them. There was no saving myself, but I couldn't bear the thought of her swinging from the gallows beside me. So, I would hang for us both.

******

As the hangman approached me unseen from the rear, the familiar scent of warm soda bread filled my nostrils. I felt gentle hands place the rough hemp rope over my head. I thought it peculiar there was no black hood. I wondered why, as it was customary to hood the condemned. Nothing seemed to be making sense at the moment. The noose was tightened *above* my Adam's apple, not below it, as it should have been. The knot was placed directly behind my head instead of behind the right ear. *This is all wrong. The rope is set too high on my throat. With the knot where it is, the fall won't snap my neck. I'll dangle here for hours, slowly strangling. Am I so detestable as to deserve this fate?* I thought to myself, until I heard the sweet voice of my beloved Desdemona whisper in my ear.

"When that rope gives way where I cut it, love, run straight over the bluffs in front of us," she said, undoing the bonds on my wrists. "At this point, it's only twelve feet down to the beach. Head for the shore. There is a zodiac with an outboard motor waiting for us there. The crew has the Groaza four hundred yards offshore, just under the surface, awaiting our arrival."

"Where shall we go?" I asked.

"The universe and all of time is your oyster," she said.

"I'm afraid you'll have to decide, my love. I'm a bit preoccupied at the moment."

"There is a Spanish galleon full of gold off the coast of Florida on planet Earth in the year 1715," she said, giggling. "I think we should take it again."

I was grinning broadly at the captain of the Crown's Forces when I heard the lever pulled and the floor disappear beneath my feet. As I dropped through the aperture of the gallows, I heard the sweet and satisfying sound of a rope snapping in two.

About the Author
Michael O'Keefe

Michael O'Keefe is a novelist, poet, and playwright from Farmingdale by way of NYC. A retired homicide Detective from the NYPD, he worked the toughest neighborhoods in New York. He was born and raised on the dangerous streets he writes about, and really never left.

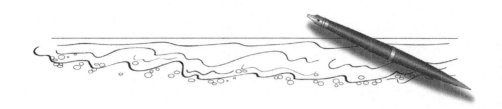

THE DISASTER EFFECT

by

Angela Reich

Offshore Savannah
- 1838 -

She saw him last. Their eyes connected momentarily as she sank softly into the deep.

Now he drifted, and like a lullaby that lapped with the swell and ebb of the waves so gentle, the salty warm sea embraced him. Losing his will to consciousness, he was lulled to sleep again and again. The rocking of the sea, irresistible siren, tempted him to the nether world, to release and retreat to the eternal... into the depths of her eyes where all was peace, fluid ease and contentment.

Then sudden shouts pierced his delirium: "There!" The man pointed out to the others. "Over yonder! Wreckage!"

The voices were distant and strange to him. Not willing to awaken, to lose the feeling of calm and peace, he resisted the jarring voices. Nearer and nearer, louder the voices came. "...And a body on board! Someone's there! On the planks!"

He began to awaken and now felt the familiar pain, like sharp knives on his blistered skin, eyes swollen shut from exposure to the relentless sun. He felt again the pain of his bruises and the stinging of the open sores washed incessantly by the salty water.

Now, the rough voices close, coming upon him, "Ahoy! Ahoy, boy! Who's there?"

Then he felt the rough movement of the splintered planks upon which he lay. And strong hands grasped him and swept him upward, his body limp, his mind still only half aware.

Routed now from his makeshift raft, awake and in shock, the horror of the disaster rushed back to him. The ship breaking apart, all passengers cast mercilessly into the sea. He tried to cry out to his rescuers, but with cracked parched lips and swollen tongue, no sound came. He gave in to the strong arms that lifted him now.

"Whose child?" The deep shout pierced the air to other survivors who were floating upon the Pulaski's sturdy hatch. Above the tumult, he heard a familiar voice respond.

"He's mine!" came the reply, "Charles! He's my boy!"

Comforting arms, his father embraced him and wept, "My brave, brave boy!" Already knowing that his wife and five other children did not survive, he was astounded and grateful to hold his son. All he had left now was Charles.

"A blanket! Is there a dry blanket for the boy?" his father shouted to the others.

His aunt, among the handful of survivors, came forward to wrap him snug. No longer drifting on the wide sea alone, and feeling the comfort of others, he sat bundled in the blanket, and in the arms of his aunt, he fell, then, into a deep, deep slumber.

******

Eight years have passed, and so much has changed since that day of the disaster.

And now Charles, a young man, looking trim and severe, rode along the rough road in his carriage after his visit to his father's new home. There, the meeting was held that settled the future of the Lamar's family businesses.

The tailored effect of Charles' white starched collar stiff against his trim red beard belied the look of the tousled hair that he allowed to stray wild and unkempt.

113

Bright blue eyes, usually sharp and disdainful, could cloud into sadness when weak moments of reverie overcame him. He girded himself against showing this vulnerable side that no one must ever see.

To all he knew, he was a study in contrasts. He confounded business rivals, appearing soft spoken yet bold and aggressive in action and effect. Socially belligerent among men, yet the ultimate southern gentleman with ladies he would charm, kissing their hands and smiling with feigned warmth.

Now, Charles' mettle has been tested, and proven to prevail against his father, whose new life seemed to attempt to erase the memories of his mother and true family; this new life for father, conducted as if the Pulaski had never happened. The new Mrs. Gazaway Lamar, older than Charles by only a few years, ran the home with orderliness and effectiveness, and now was busily making the nursery ready for the first child born to their new family.

Charles was used to his father's efficiency in all situations. Since a small boy, he watched his father create an empire. His one plantation expanded into three, all resting sixteen miles upstream from Savannah Harbor. There, crops were harvested and sailed downriver to his own wharf complex that buzzed with intensity. A six-story rice mill removed husks and bran from the rice kernels, while presses baled the cotton, and warehouses stood ready to store all while awaiting shipment, each operation run by Gazaway himself.

Today's meeting secured Charles' future. All of Gazaway Lamar's Savannah businesses have now been turned over officially and legally to Charles. His father, happy now in his new life, has moved on in business as well, with banking as his new venture.

Charles ruminated on all this as he gazed out of the carriage window at the mosses swaying gently from the roadside trees. The horses snorted as they faithfully pulled his carriage steadily along the rutted road toward his new future, as his own man.

******

Gazaway Lamar's entire family was aboard the Pulaski the fateful day that his newest steam yacht was to sail a sea route from Savannah to Baltimore. He had been consumed with his plan to create a whole steam line based upon this prototype.

The Pulaski would be the solution to his frustration about the downward trend of southern business. Plantations had to ship their cotton bales to New York, which were then loaded onto powerful transatlantic steamships for the voyage to factories in Liverpool. There, southern cotton was manufactured into clothing, and loaded onto ships for a return voyage to New York to be sold in American marketplaces.

Gazaway Lamar knew the only way for southern plantations to retain full profits from their own raw materials was to control the transport of its cotton. That was an awesome task.

First, the Savannah River had to be cleared of the blockades put there to secure the river mouth from British invaders during the Revolutionary War. Whole scale dredging was needed then to make it into a deep-water port to open it to meaningful trade. Then Lamar would be able to use his own line of steam-powered trans-Atlantic vessels to transport his cotton to Liverpool.

Only then would he brook no further interference by the North in his ability to make a profit. Control of a southern sea route to Liverpool was his only option.

Gazaway Lamar's schemes were never known to fail. His investors brimmed with expectation.

After the Pulaski's three test voyages along the coast, this journey would serve as her maiden passenger voyage. The thrill of excitement was everywhere. All came from near and far to witness the launch and to see all the first families of the South, the select few who would be the pioneers, witnesses to the cutting edge of ocean travel.

116

Barely able to contain his curiosity while waiting with the others on the wharf, fourteen-year-old Charles begged his Mother, "Please? May I go aboard now?" he remembered.

She nodded her approval, warning, "But don't interfere with the workers. They are all very busy now."

On board, the housekeeping staff readied the luxurious staterooms, appointed with the finest upholstery and furniture. Guests' trunks were being emptied and placed in handsomely carved armoires, garden flowers displayed on every available surface, drapes opened to allow the shore breeze to freshen the room and let the sun glisten upon every exquisite detail.

The kitchen staff were busily checking and double-checking the inventory of meats, fresh fruits and vegetables. The chefs' menus, meant to astound, required intricate and rare ingredients, precious and delicate.

Meanwhile, the dining room staff inspected the stores of finest china, looking for any chip or crack from the transport onto the ship, polishing and cleaning the ornate silver service, buffing the glittering crystal so that a rainbow of color emanated from each goblet and glass.

But Charles was most interested in what was going on below decks. The smell and noise of the machinery in the engine room, the gears and mechanics and the power of the immense boilers fascinated him.

There, the First Engineer reviewed the procedure for running and maintaining this newest technology in steam travel with all crew, old and new alike. "This series of steps cannot be emphasized enough," he commanded sharply. "The engines are extremely powerful, but also extremely sensitive," he warned. "All procedures must be followed exactly. No exceptions." The boilermaker there on staff nodded in assent, adding, "It is a matter of life and death."

Charles then ran up the stairs to the upper level where the two hundred feet of the Pulaski offered its guests the pleasure of the ocean breeze on its spacious decks. A wide, open promenade rested above a main deck for strolling, mingling, socializing, and relaxing on plush, upholstered settees. Elegance and comfort awaited the passengers, no detail left unattended.

There, he leaned over the rail to see townspeople gathered on the dock to catch sight of the ship and to watch for all the richest families of the South. Electric with excitement, the murmurs from the crowd grew to distinct cries when the Pulaski's engines released a loud burst of steam from its twin smokestacks.

The men clamored, "The latest technology! The fastest vessel!"

The ladies cried, "There! There is Mr. Lamar! So handsome! And his wife, such elegant clothes!"

All passengers inched forward on the dock, ready to board. Fine silks rustled past the onlookers, splendid silver threaded brocades, hats, purses, and jewelry gleamed in the Savannah sunlight, ladies shimmered like royals, attended by their maids, their trunks carried by porters.

The onlookers all watched Gazaway and his wife, the small children trailing with their aunt, the first family to board the vessel as they made their way up the steep ramp. There at its summit, Gazaway turned to face the crowd. He waved down the cheers, and into the hushed upturned faces, he shouted, "The hold of New York Harbor on control of southern cotton must end," he declared. Cheers rose from the crowd. He continued, "Now we shall develop our own port, and make our own trade routes to Liverpool with a new steam line, and keep our own profits for ourselves!" His booming voice cast its spell over every passenger and onlooker.

A short hush, then the crowd erupted into roars and shouts of approval, knowing this man's vision will mean better lives for them all.

The Lamars were followed by others of the wealthy elite climbing the ramp, eager to be a part of this historic moment. Eager, also, to claim the bragging rights of such an event. To be able to say with pride, "Oh, yes... certainly we were on that voyage. What luxury! What excitement! All the best people were there, of course. What a thrill!"

Late that night, after the tinkling of delicate crystal champagne glasses and the clatter of silver against china in the dining room grew quiet, many of the revelers wended their way sleepily to their staterooms where they felt confident the obliging sea would lull them to sleep on their soft feather mattresses.

A few of the men left the dining room and made their way up to the promenade. They, with glasses of fine brandy, would finish their conversations and enjoy the gentle sea breeze that carried the sound of their satisfied murmurs and hearty laughter into the night, the aroma of fine cigars lingering in the light breeze. Aboard the Pulaski, the first day's sail seemed to yield to an evening of ease and peace.

But below decks, a scene of another kind was brewing.

"The alarm!" roared the First Engineer. "Can't you hear it, by God! Wake up!" he bellowed as he ran toward the engine room.

"Whaaa?" The attendant on watch jerked to his feet and saw that the water had completely boiled off in the starboard engine.

In a panic to cool it down, he jerked the red handle fully open and flooded the red-hot boiler with cold seawater. "NOOOO!" shouted the First Engineer as he ran to correct the error. But, he was too late...

A deafening blast jarred the sea, seeming as if the earth itself had split in two. The boiler's explosion shredded everything around it. The promenade deck above the engine room splintered into shards that sailed high, rising like thousands of arrows into the sky. And on deck, the shattered boiler shot its deadly shrapnel, piercing all within reach, and tearing a hole in the ship's starboard hull through which the boiler's remains descended like lead into the depths.

The blast cut the Pulaski in half amidships. Into the ship's shattered side gushed the surrounding sea. Then, with agonizing groans of steel and sharp cracks of splintering timber, the bow and stern each raised slowly, implausibly, until straight up, fore and aft decks nearly vertical, seeming to fold upward like a butterfly's wings alight. Collapsing walls, bursting windows, cries of terror, all the world collided in terrible motion and sound upon the silent sea, under the watchful stars and the few, unshaken clouds that drifted across the night sky.

Then a strange stillness, an eerie hush, as if the Pulaski hesitated against nature's hold. But, the sea, ruling

121

element, was victorious. A deafening whoosh and whirling violence of the clash between ship and sea and the Pulaski sank mercilessly into the dark deep, taking all within reach down into its pitiless, swirling vortex, there, thirty miles out to sea, where only the stars were bright witnesses on that tragic night.

For Charles, days adrift and alone, clinging to the ship's shattered planks.

******

Although the years have passed, the terror of that day still lives in his memory.

The long journey from his father's house nearly at an end, Charles dozed in the carriage, the clip-clop of the horses' hooves hitting the hard packed dirt road in even time. The humid breeze passing through the gently rocking carriage, the swaying of the coach brought to his mind the lazy lull of the sea all those years ago when he lay for days aboard the ship's splintered wreckage. Now, in calm repose was when memories, usually kept buried, crept out of his unconscious and delivered the pain anew.

His mind replayed the deafening blast. The echoes of screams and panic. The rush of seawater. The huge vessel sidewise, and he, striving against the crush of terrified men and women as they fought their way down the stairs to the main deck, swarming toward the lifeboats. But

Charles battled against them to go up the stairs to the second deck, to the rooms of his brothers and sister, to get them out of the doomed vessel and away from danger.

He led the children in the night's darkness, then overboard and into the cold, salty sea. There he heard the screams of his mother, and attempted to make way toward her among the wreckage. Within earshot now, she cried out, "My babies! My loves! Listen to Charles. He can help you!" The children all tried to cling together, to keep each other afloat. Charles, responsible, the eldest of four young brothers, one small sister.

Treading water, twisting, turning toward each wretched cry, "Help! Help me Charles!" and "Mother! Help me!" their small voices were delivered into the black night. He gasped against mouthfuls of sea, shouting out each of the children's names, shouting in panic, "Hold on! Hold onto one another!"

The memory of their small, cold, wet hands. Their delicate fingers slipping from his, each child, one by one, his grasp unable to hold tight enough, his efforts futile while his siblings sank one by one, thrashing, as he and his mother urgently called, reaching out now to the empty air, the merciless sea claiming each in turn.

Then, Charles alone, witnessed the final horrible quiet, as Mother too, exhausted and helpless, descended silently into the deep.

For Charles, the last to see his mother alive. To see her terrified eyes as she sank.

Her eyes. She saw him last.

******

He startled awake now, as he usually did, with each re-surfacing of the terror, his blue eyes soft and filled with tears. Realizing he was nearly at his destination, he wiped them with quick, rough motions until they regained their appearance of aloof detachment.

His carriage stopped at the wharf. He surveyed the river and observed the Lamar barges as they docked. He watched the men unloading rice and cotton, his mind swiftly calculating profits. On the wharf, the men, his men, labored in the hot Georgia sun.

He nimbly descended the carriage. The workers paused to tip their hats, their eyes cast downward in deference, bearing their sweaty brows, their labor, all his. But Charles' cold blue eyes saw them only with indifference.

Stiff and straight-backed, chin held high, he strode confidently to his office on the wharf. Charles commands all he surveys, convinced now that he is invincible.

About the Author
Angela Reich

Angela Reich serves as docent for New York's historical Fire Island Lighthouse. As an independent researcher, she lectures on Long Island's maritime history. A Ph.D. in literature, Reich has published literary criticism on John Milton's *Paradise Regained*. SHIPWRECK OF HOPES is frst historical fction.

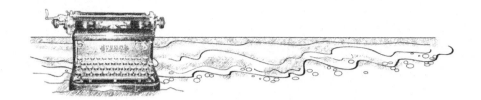

TREASURES LOST AND FOUND

by

Patricia Walsh

Juliette gazed out of the car window, watching the landscape pass by. This was going to be her first visit to her family's ancestral home, which she had only heard of in stories regaled over the years. She was the great, great, great granddaughter of one of the first occupants of the Bay Island mansion. The original house was built in late 1600's, for a prominent ship builder and his family. Situated on the south shore of Long Island it had commanding views of the Great South Bay and Fire Island.

As the car drew closer, Juliette was getting nervous. Long Island was nothing like the Midwest. It was just 6 months ago that she was told she was the last surviving relative of the family legacy, and she inherited Bay Island. With no ties to hold her in North Dakota, she decided to move to her ancestral home. Being a historian gave her the

129

opportunity to work from anywhere, and what better place to work her magic. It was Juliette's intent to explore every nook and cranny of her new home. She would uncover more of its history and what it had to offer, documenting and adding to what had already been written.

As Juliette stepped onto the back porch she could feel the sigh of relief from the house, grateful that it once again would be occupied. Fitting the ancient key into the door, it swung open, the whoosh of air embracing her. She expected to smell the odor of years gone by, but instead was met by the smell of fine wood, polish and fresh linens. Thankfully, the housekeeper had taken good care of Bay Island. From the smells emanating from the kitchen the housekeeper had also left a hearty meal for her dinner. The larder and fridge were stocked, leaving Juliette the task of unpacking and some time to rest up from her long, arduous journey.

Up early, with the sun streaming into the bedroom window, she got her bearings and realized that she was now the lady of the mansion. She had chosen the Proprietor's Suite as her bedroom. After all, it had been the sanctuary of one of her distant relatives before his death. Through the years other family members had also used the room. She loved being among their personal items, the awards, paintings, photographs and items from their travels abroad. But, her first order of business after her coffee, of course, was to try and find the eagle and replica ship that had disappeared over the years. Despite all of the stories from years ago, none of them held any clues to the origin, or age of the ship or eagle, just that they had mysteriously disappeared. Though the years her relatives had lamented over their loss. There was no recollection of what rooms they might have been in either, nor were there any photographs. It was as though they never existed. But Juliette knew they did, and she would uncover the mystery.

Juliette knew it would take some time to go through Bay Island, not just days, or weeks, but months. There were three floors and forty-eight rooms, not including the two attics and cavernous basement, with its many hidden corners. She would have to take her time, go room by room, searching every nook and cranny as she explored. Month after month, she thoroughly explored the rooms, making notes of interest and cataloging the contents. Sadly, none of the rooms contained the missing ship replica or the eagle.

Months later, after many weeks of lifting and sifting, Juliette came across a set of keys among the items left behind by past descendants. They were obviously door keys, from the look and sizes. Juliette had by this time explored all of the rooms and decided to go floor by floor, room by room, to identify and mark the keys. Many keys were tried and matched to their rooms, a daunting task to say the least. When she reached the desolate third floor, she followed the same procedure as on the other floors. Stepping into one of the rooms in the servants' quarters she turned the key to unlock a closet. To her surprise there was another locked door within the closet, behind the vintage apparel left behind. Apparently no one knew this door existed, or it had long been forgotten.

With the remaining keys on the ring, Juliette's hands shook as she turned a key inside the old lock, hoping it would click open. Wide-eyed with surprise, the darkness revealed a long hidden room. It had been years since this room was opened. The room was thick with cobwebs suspended from the rafters, glistening in the sunlight that peeked through a lone circular window at the end of the small room. Finding a pull chain from a single swaying light bulb, Juliette was able to momentarily illuminate the small room, before the light went out and darkness again engulfed her. Blinking her eyes to adjust to the dim light that was streaming through the small window, she saw an old trunk. With adrenaline coursing through her veins, Juliette stepped into the darkness to open the old trunk, which was locked. Once again she tried one of the remaining keys, jumping as the key turned in the cylinder, revealing a large suitcase, locked just like the old trunk had been. With the keys digging into the palm of her hand she hoped for the best, as she tried more of the remaining keys. All of a sudden the key and lock became one, and the suitcase sprang open. The suitcase contained what looked like old household records and deeds. Digging deeper into the contents her fingers brushed against something hard. Holding her breath she removed the packages, unwrapping them carefully. Stunned, Juliette fell back on her knees when the long lost ship replica and eagle were revealed. Searching through the paperwork she tried to discover who might have hidden them, and why. Sadly, her search did not reveal any other information.

Ship and eagle in hand, Juliette backed out of the room sighing as she locked the door and rearranged the clothes that had kept it hidden. There was nothing to say, there was no explanation. It was obvious; she was meant to find this room. This was one secret Juliette was keeping to herself! The ship and the eagle have once again have taken their rightful spot in the Bay Island Mansion.

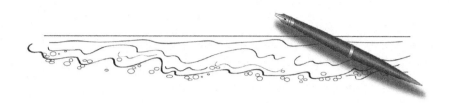

THEY ENTERED THE "PROGRAM"

by

Patricia Walsh

Buster and Minnie sat on the deck overlooking the pool. It was finally nice enough to enjoy the outdoors. They had not seen each other for a while. Even though they were family they tried to keep their time together to a minimum since entering the Witness Protection Program. The last thing they needed was to have anyone recognize them. But their get together was more than the two cousins socializing. They had just found out that the Windsor Avenue house had been sold.

Sipping on their beverages, a beer for Buster, and a Pink Pussycat for Minnie, they knew they had to plan their last heist. Thinking back to their heydays as part of the El Gatos gang, they remembered the last break-in and heist. The El Gatos were the terror of the D.C. area, especially around the National Mall. Minnie remembered it well, getting caught, she and Buster turning states evidence and then the "Program." The El Gatos' were all cousins. They were part of a bigger family, who will remain nameless. Back in the day they were known as El Chivato (the sneak), Chica Bonita (pretty girl), Kincado, Dulce Sabine, Gustavo, and Un Ojo Sam (One-eye Sam). Las Chica's (the girls), and La Rata (the rat).

It was in the Smithsonian Museum of Natural History, in the Hall of Geology, where they first saw the gems. El Chivato was perfect for the break-in, with his cargo vest, fake badge, and aviator sunglasses. He fit into the crowd, looking like he was part of security. While the others were the lookouts planted by each entrance, they released La Rata, whose scurrying sent the security beams off, which kept the guards occupied. Chica Bonita, the cat burglar grabbed the jewels for El Chivato to secure in the cargo pockets of his vest. What they did not know was that they were being followed for months. Luckily, the Las Chicas were able to hide the gems, which were never found. The rest is history. To avoid life imprisonment El Chivato (Buster), and Chica Bonita (Minnie), turned state's evidence and were given a chance to go into the Witness Protection Program. Now all of the other members were gone, except for El Chivato, Chica Bonita, Las Chicas, and La Rata. Buster and Minnie settled on the South Shore of Long Island. Las Chicas were now known as "the girls" and La Rata, goes by "Blinkie". They fit in perfectly, among their peers.

Now with the Windsor Avenue home sold, Buster and Minnie knew what they had to do. It seems that the Las Chicas hid the gems in the vast basement of the old house. With its many nooks and crannies it was the perfect hiding place. They never thought that Maria and Grandma Jo would sell the house. They must find a way to retrieve the gems without anyone knowing. A visit to Grandmas Jo's needed to happen, and fast, before the basement was emptied. If they helped empty the basement it would give them access to the areas.

Buster and Minnie searched high and low with no sign of the missing gems. Finally cleaning out the last cubby under stairs they saw the gray pouch hidden among some old nuts and bolts. Buster tried to stuff the pockets of his cargo vest as fast as he could while Minnie kept Grandma Jo occupied. The pouch was too big for his pockets, so he had to remove the gems and put them different pockets of his cargo vest. Perfect, Minnie thought as she let her breath out. Everything was going according to plan, mission accomplished or so they thought. Running up the basement steps Buster stumbled on the top step, one pocket of his vest unsnapped, sending a cat's eye gem rolling to the bottom of the stairs, landing at Grandma Jo's feet. "What is this," she asked. Buster and Minnie froze. Aw shit, minutes from a clean get away. Grandma Jo can never know about their past. So, Buster and Minnie did what they did best. Looking at each other sheepishly they proclaimed, "It was going to be a new eye for one-eye Sam"!

About the Author
Patricia Walsh

Ms. Walsh resides on Long Island where she enjoys dining out, cooking, travel, writing, spending time with her family and exploring her creative side. She also serves on the Board of Trustees for a local historical society. She is the author of Wizecatz and Dogz. She is currently working another book.

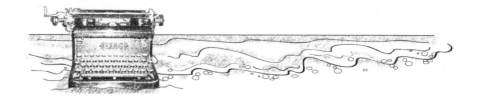

THE FORTUNE TELLER

by

Elaine Kiesling Whitehouse

The neon light in the fortune teller's window glared crimson in the gray drizzle of the evening rush hour. "Psychic Reader, Palm and Tarot" it said. Subway commuters hurried past, their heads bent under umbrellas.

Esmeralda peered out the rain-streaked window. She doubted there would be any business tonight. She closed the curtain and sat on the faded, red velvet sofa in the tiny, cluttered room. The heavy scent of incense clung to the damp air. Postcards from Europe, fans from China and stacks of magazines were among the room's clutter.

An ornate, gilt clock hung on the wall opposite the sofa, ticking the time away. Under the clock were shelves containing a statue of the Virgin Mary, a worn copy of the Bible and a tome called *The Magic Mirror of Michael Nostradamus*. Other than the neon sign, a small quartz lamp provided the only illumination in the room. Beside the lamp lay a silver letter opener and a letter with a foreign stamp.

Behind a faded green and maroon tapestry, a rocking chair creaked. The rhythmic creaking and the ticking of the gilt clock were the only sounds in the room. Tick, tick, tick. Creak, creak, creak. It was the same every night, for all her adult life, the endless sound marking the passage of time, the passage of her life, as Esmeralda waited for someone to walk in the door.

Then she observed a woman cross the street and pause in front of the sign. She seemed curious, as if wondering whether she should dare to enter. Esmeralda got up and went to the window. She smiled at the woman and beckoned her to come in. The woman hesitated for a moment, and then opened the door.

"Welcome," said Esmeralda warmly. She took her coat and umbrella. The coat was of good quality and the umbrella was a man's. "Would you like the cards or a palm reading?" Esmeralda indicated the sofa, inviting the woman to sit down.

"Well, I don't know," said the woman. "I've never done this before." She looked around furtively, as if worrying that someone might see her there.

Esmeralda sized her up quickly and said the price was twenty dollars for a palm reading. She smiled at the woman again, observing her carefully. She was about thirty-five, blonde, blue-eyed, with a turned-down mouth and a crease between her eyes. A wedding band and a plain watch were her only jewelry. She was well dressed but not extravagantly so. Neither her hair nor nails had been professionally cared for in the recent past. She fidgeted with her purse and sat with tightly crossed legs.

"I don't know why I came in," she blurted out. "Maybe it was the rain. I didn't want to get wet . . ."

"Try to relax," said Esmeralda soothingly, her voice like silk. She pushed her long, dark hair off her shoulders so that it hung down her back, out of the way. The neon light cast a reddish glow on her smooth skin, revealing a faint scar that ran down the length of her left jaw. "Put the money between your palms, close your eyes and make a wish," she said.

The woman looked around the room for a moment. Esmeralda thought she might ask about the incessant creaking of the rocking chair. Tonight, it seemed louder than ever.

The woman said, "I feel so foolish."

"Why should you?" asked Esmeralda. "Make a wish. Do not tell me what it is." Esmeralda studied the woman as she sat with her eyes tightly closed, the twenty-dollar bill resting between her palms in her lap. Esmeralda

143

surmised that the woman worked at a professional job and worried about the usual things – debts, her work, her marriage, perhaps her children. Maybe she was involved in an extramarital affair. All the problems of life were common to Esmeralda. She heard about them every day.

"Now, open your eyes and hold out your hands."

The woman did as she was told. Esmeralda deftly removed the twenty dollars and quickly pocketed it. Then she examined both palms of the woman, tracing lines with her left hand. With her right index finger and thumb, she held the tip of the woman's ring finger.

"You have a long lifeline," she said. "You will live to be eighty or beyond." She looked at the woman. Her face was blank.

"You spend money, sometimes wisely, sometimes foolishly." Again, she observed the woman for a reaction. There was none.

Esmeralda traced her left forefInger along various lines on the woman's palm, predicting that the woman would continue to enjoy good health, and that she would be traveling soon. Esmeralda spoke soothingly, hypnotically, her voice rising and falling in rhythm with the creaking of the rocking chair, exploring topics she hoped would produce a reaction. She watched the pupils of the woman's eyes. All the while the tip of the woman's ring finger rested lightly between Esmeralda's fingers.

Abruptly, the woman asked, "Who is behind that curtain?"

"My mother," said Esmeralda.

As if jolted by an electrical charge, the woman's finger jerked involuntarily.

Esmeralda said nothing for a moment, her own heart beginning to quicken. "You are wondering about your own mother."

"Yes," whispered the woman. Her pupils widened perceptibly.

"She is causing you some distress."

"Yes, yes!" said the woman, breathing faster.

A small pulse began drumming in Esmeralda's left temple. Her eyes glittered like coals.

"I want to know. . ." the woman's voice faltered."Tell me, please," coaxed Esmeralda. "I can help." She stared into the woman's eyes. How to answer this one? Difflcult. Painful.

"Your mother has been ill a long time," guessed Esmeralda.

The woman nodded.

"Yet her heart is strong." The woman's fInger twitched slightly between Esmeralda's.

"I can tell you that your mother will live as long as her heart remains strong, but unfortunately, she will continue to suffer. If you come tomorrow night, we can light candles and consult the spirits about your mother's remaining time on earth."

The woman's eyes filled with tears.

"This is sad for you," said Esmeralda. The rain was pouring down now, drowning out the sound of the clock's ticking, but the rattan chair creaked and creaked, faster than before.

Esmeralda said, "Ask me one more question. Then return tomorrow, and we will consult the spirits."

The woman shook her head. "I do not want to consult the spirits." The tears were brimming over now. "What I really want to know . . ."

Esmeralda held her hand more firmly and placed her hand on the woman's arm. "Tell me," she said. "What is it you want to know about your mother?" Esmeralda's hypnotic eyes held the gaze of the woman's as if the two were wrapped together in a trance.

"I want to know," whispered the woman, "I want to know why my mother never loved me."

146

Esmeralda's mouth felt suddenly dry, and the blood drained from her face. She let go of the woman's hand. She noticed that the creaking had stopped. The only sound now was the icy rain furiously pelting the window glass. The rapid pulse in the woman's throat seemed to match her own. When Esmeralda spoke again, her voice was no longer soothing. It was as dry and brittle as straw.

"You are wrong," she said. "Your mother always loved you. Maybe she never told you so. Maybe she rejected you. But your mother loved you before and she loves you now, despite what she did to you."

"How do you know this?" whispered the woman.

The neon light glinted red in Esmeralda's eyes, and she smiled, drawing back her lips, for the first time revealing pointy little teeth.

"I know," said Esmeralda," because I am a psychic."

The woman breathed deeply. "Thank you," she said, getting up. "You have helped."

No, thought Esmeralda. You have helped.

The woman said nothing more. She walked out the door and disappeared into the rainy black night.

Esmeralda sighed a long sigh and sat on the worn sofa, looking at all the knickknacks and breathing in the claustrophobic air. Then she stood up walked over to the table with the quartz lamp and put the letter with the foreign stamp into her pocket. She opened the closet door and took out a small, dusty suitcase. She put on her coat and took her umbrella. She noticed that the rain was starting to subside. Then she turned off the neon sign and walked out the door, closing it behind her for the last time.

About the Author
Elaine Kiesling Whitehouse

Elaine Kiesling Whitehouse is an award-winning journalist and former editor of the *Fire Island Tide*. Elaine obtained her master's degree in international Relations at the Maxwell School of Syracuse University. She has written three works of historical fiction. Her latest book, *Psoline,* was published in 2021.

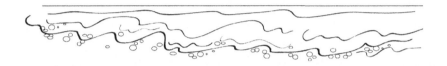

poetry

THE FABRIC

by

David B. Axelrod

The fabric of the universe is
a silken cloth but it protects us.

Some wear it as sackcloth,
rend their shirt to mourn.

Others pull tight the hooded
string hiding their ethnicity.

Only, DNA differs so little
between us, we are universal.

The fabric is tightly woven
though tiny threads pull bare.

Our politics, religions are
hardly wrinkles in space-time.

As if skin color or the right church
makes us a better tailor.

From the fabric of the universe
no flag need be woven.

SPRING CHICKENS
by
David B. Axelrod

On their 65th Anniversary.

He hovers over her, a rooster
not afraid to be a mother hen.
At their age, you'd think
they'd be walking on egg shells,
but there's nothing chicken
about them, though they both
admit, "aging is not for the meek."
After sixty-five years together
they still live free-range lives,
out on the town. See them walking
arm and arm, kissing publicly,
cracking jokes, tickling each
other's fancy. No egg on these
faces. No one can coop up this love.

FLORIDA HIBISCUS

by

David B. Axelrod

Seditious shrubs
caught surging
past their borders,
dressed in raucous
colors. Unwilling
to chose a season,
they bloom all year.
Hybrids with fancy
names — "Dinnerplate,"
with its variegated
palate. Or deep,
red petals of "Holy
Grail." Some are
said to heal —
make a stronger
heart, slow our
aging. Others
lie back in
inadvertent beds
like hibiscus'
quiet cousin,
Rose of Sharon,
flourishing
by any door

155

POLYSEMY

(The coexistence of many possible meanings)

by

David B. Axelrod

I pretend I can augur our future,
but I know how you quiet me.
When I'm hot or bothered,
you are my cool, calm days —
antidote to splenetic ways
that otherwise would sear
my options. If I can't play,
you offer me a rain dates.

Weather forecasters, should
be cast as clowns not seers.
Rather than guess,
they should eschew revanchism —
teach us to accept imprecision
without regrets or revenge.
With you, there are certainly
bright days ahead for me.

About the Author
Dr. David B. Axelrod

Dr. David B. Axelrod was Suffolk County, Long Island's and is now Volusia County, Florida's, Poet Laureate (appointed for 2015-2023). For his third Fulbright, he was the first Poet Laureate in the People's Republic of China. His twenty-third book of poetry is *Mother Tongue*. Read more at his website:

www.poetrydoctor.org

BURIED ALIVE

by

Cindi Sansone-Braff

There are people we bury
Long before they die.
Life,
Fights,
Circumstances,
Communal conventions,
Imagined slights,
All This
And
Then some
Spawn the schism.
These once cherished,
Long-lost souls
Haunt us,
Whispering in the wee still hours,
"Evermore."
Like persistent poltergeists
Uninvited
Yet
Secretly
Welcomed,

They recklessly roam
About the dimmed
And
Darkened hallways
Of our leaden hearts,
Whispering in the dreamscape,
"Forevermore."
They consistently
Careen the corridors
Of our consciousness,
Breathing
Regret
Remorse
Retrospection
Into our being.
Time and time again,
These ravenous révenants
Taunt us,
Whispering in the wintry winds,
"Nevermore."
"Nevermore."
"Nevermore."

About the Author
Cindi Sansone-Braff

Cindi Sansone-Braff is an award-winning playwright. She has a BFA in Theatre from UCONN and is a member of the Dramatists Guilds. She is the author of *Grant Me a Higher Love*, *Why Good People Can't Leave Bad Relationships*, and *Confessions of a Reluctant Long Island Psychic*.

www.Grantmeahigherlove.com.

UKRAINE (A POEM FOR PEACE)

by

Theresa Dodaro

The tightrope walker gingerly takes one step at a time,

Below him, cities are bombed by missiles launched from far
and wide,

The children cry for their fathers who were left behind,

The mothers clutch their children and wonder where their
futures lie.

The tightrope walker takes another step as the rope beneath
him shakes,

His divided country judges every step and for him to falter
they wait,

Some are more worried about the price of gas than of the
nuclear war at stake,

They live their lives in their warm houses, with full bellies,
they are safe.

The conductor watches the destruction from his high tower,

He orders the trumpets to sound their advance, the drums
beat on,

He ignores the sounds of protest and twists the reality with
his total power,

His people believe the lies told by their leader,
a master of the con.

The conductor's audience applaud him like a faithful
daughter,

They care not what the world sees and hears,

They follow him like blind sheep to the slaughter,

The music of their conductor drowns out any of their fears.

The comedian juggles and sends out to the world a desperate
call,

He disputes the ridiculous claim against him of Nazism,

Bravely he stands up to the conductor as the bombs continue
to fall,

Begging the tightrope walker to traverse the chasm of
totalitarianism.

The battered people fight with fortitude for their lives and hopes,

The mouse against the lion once again rises up and roars,

But the children now lie in the streets in blood-soaked pink puffer coats,

Peace, life, freedom urges them on, for this is their cause.

About the Author
Theresa Dodaro

Author, Theresa Dodaro, holds a BA in liberal arts from Stony Brook University. She worked in publishing and marketing until she put her career on hold to raise her children. Now that her children are grown, she spends her time writing novels, blogging, and conducting genealogical research for herself and others.

NEATH THE MOON AND THE STARS

by

Adrienne Falzon

Somewhere there's a Muslim child

Neath the moon and the stars

Somewhere there's a Hebrew child

Neath the moon and the stars

Somewhere there's a Christian child

Neath the moon and the stars

No different from you and I

Neath the moon and the stars

The God they love

Is the same for all

The God they love

Wants the best for all

The God they love

Made us all to be

All so different

Yet in unity

We do not choose

Where we appear

We do not choose

What we hold dear

This land, that land

Who knows where

We arrived

Without a care

Somehow, somewhere we are born

As Christian, Muslim, Christian be.

We are what's given

don't you see?

This Church, that Mosque, this Temple, too

Serve God the same for me and you

A God who sees us all as ONE

A God who wants us to BE ONE

ONE for Him

And ONE for all

Rich man, poor man

Short or tall

The way we pray

And when we do

Has no effect

On me and you

As long as love

Is in our heart

How could that

Keep us apart?

171

Our skins may vary
Our countries too
Histories and culture
Make quite a stew

A stew that's made
With all the blends
To be enjoyed
With us as friends

One part alone
Would never quite do
When put together
We have quite a stew!

There's beauty in learning
Other ways to express
What we have in our hearts
Rather duress

172

Other ways, giving chances
In learning to live
With people with whom
We can share and to give

The path on our journey
As God intended it so
Was to respect all who love Him
With no hatred or foe

If we truly love God
As we say that we do
We must accept other ways
People do what they do
If only we realized
We're all quite the same
No matter the face
No matter the name
Why is there fighting?

Can we think of its trace?

Cause we worship our God

In a whole other place?

How sad for our God

For all He has done

In creating our world

To have it undone!

Let's try to all find the fun

To learn from each and everyone

To learn from people near and far

To make us better at who we are

To accept all, we cannot lose

No need to win, no need to choose

There are no winners in a war

There is no peace in keeping score

Children learn from us, you know

When we show love, they will grow

When we show hate

It seals their fate

But at the heart of every creed

There is a call to love

Put there, to be sure,

From our Lord above

Yes, at the heart of each of us

A yearning does exist

To live in peace and feel secure

So why do we resist?

Yes, love of all can be the way

To cure the broken heart

Love of all gives peace a chance

And life a brand-new start

Neath the same moon and stars we go

They shine for all, as we sure know

Makes no difference who you are

When you wish upon a star.

Make your wish

And hope it's true

A better world

For me and you

About the Author
Adrienne Falzon

Adrienne Falzon, author of five books, lives in Rancho Santa Fe, California, and Southampton, New York, with her husband Manny. Adrienne participates in many local charities, is a board member of the Rancho Santa Fe Garden Club, and is Co-Vice President of the Old Towne Garden Club of Southampton.

LUNCH WITH RICHARD

by

Holly Gordon

I step into your world -
my art fits into your space
and expands my vision

Books, your chosen friends
comfortably placed awaiting your touch -
Some are my friends, too

Music heard before
is listened to for the first time -
you poke at my senses

A feast has been created
artfully presented morsels fill the table -
I am stuffed too soon

Deliberate and controlled
impetuous and intuitive -
Gentle harmony of friendship

179

GIVERNY

by

Holly Gordon

Written at the end
of second stay in Giverny

Je cherche les couleurs
et la lumière
Je pense en français
sans connaître les mots
L'appareil photographique
parle pour moi
Et mon Coeur est plein.

I search for color and light
I think in French
without knowing the words
My camera speaks for me
And my heart is full.

About the Author
Holly Gordon

Holly's work is in NYU Langone, Stony Brook Hospital and Molloy College and has appeared in The New York Times and Newsday. Her book Parallel Perspectives: The Brush/Lens Collaboration discusses using technology as a creative tool. In a ground-breaking exhibition in Southampton, she is represented by Denise Bibro Fine Art.

THE SEEKER'S SECRET

by

Joel W. Harris

Once I loved too often and too well.

And oh, the stories I could tell.

They say it's a sin to love unbidden,

So, I kept my feelings carefully hidden.

Like the text of art books never read

My artful words are never said.

And yet it seldom ended there.

Sans words sans deeds to make aware

To one to whom should not be shown

Somehow my feelings not unknown

But for a while, as I endeavor

To find the one to hold forever.

When that artful feeling goes both ways

For a love that will last to the end of days.

About the Author
Joel W. Harris

Born and raised in Brooklyn and living in Woodmere for the last 58 years with my beautiful wife, Evvy. Retired from a career in insurance spanning over 60 years I continue to be an avid reader as well as a writer and have over 3,000 books in my home library.

THE SECRET WEAPON

by

Sheri Lynn

Walking past a bird bath nestled

amidst flowers and tomato plants, we

head for our bench framed by trees

rich with bird houses. Grandpa's

hunting beagles are asleep in their

kennels and don't stir as we pass.

> *Tense, I call, "Hi Grandpa, I*
>
> *will pick you up for our*
>
> *interview tomorrow."*

Owls warble and fireflies dance about us.

"Can you find the big dipper?" my

Grandmother asks.

"Is that it?" I reply, pointing.

"Yes, see the little dipper pouring into it?"

she takes my finger, outlines its path.

187

After work, I drive my
Grandfather in near silence, to
the police station. Detectives
take us to a drab room.

In her kitchen we take sweet peas
from their pods, pop several into our
mouths.
"Why doesn't Roxy sleep with the
beagles?" I ask.
"Roxy is a house dog," she replies,
handing me treats to give the tail
wagging pup.
"Why don't the beagles sleep in the house?"
"They wouldn't know how to behave.
Can you imagine them running and
jumping about like bunnies?" We fall
into giggles.

"Do you remember anything
unusual at the hospital?"

188

"No" my Grandfather replies.

With dinner in the oven, we go to her

windowed nature surround peninsula

office. In awe, I watch her fingers dart a

cross silver laced round black

typewriter keys.

> *"My wife fell into a coma and*
> *passed after a code blue.*
> *She had a simple leg injury.*
> *It doesn't make sense."*

After dinner we half-watch 60-

Minutes, chat, lather our hands with

Oil-of-Olay; I study hers - red nail

polish, a thin silver wristwatch, such

purpose and grace.

> *The detective responds, "Yes,*
> *circumstances suggest she may*
> *have been one of Angelo's victims.*

189

Tucking me in, she reads aloud our

favorite Peter Cottontail book, asks

"Do you think Peter would enjoy our

garden? Would he, his brothers and

sisters eat our carrots and cause

mischief?" as I doze, imaging us ...

Epilogue

Along with others, my Grandmother passed

a crime victim blasted on headlines. It is my *hope*,

she is remembered for how she lived. From her

December 30, 1971, editorial,

> "The Secret Weapon":

> "A small word spells the difference

> between happiness and despair...a

> word too often forgotten in the hustle

> and bustle of our pressure-filled days.

> That word is hope and, as another

> new year dawns, we would all do well

> to remember it once more."

Hope can build a dream or change a
life; it is the secret weapon of those
who have survived the depths to reach
for something better.

With it we can look forward to good
things in the year ahead....hope for
peace, for a united world at last.

The new year is sure to bring its share
of trials but with hope, we can meet
them all and make 1972 significant
in our lives.

Hope without courage and
determination won't work, of course,
but it can be the starting point...a new
beginning...and is surely worth the
try.

Let's all look ahead to a truly happy
and HOPEFUL New Year."

HERO HONOR

by

Sheri Lynn

*"The soldier above all others prays for peace, for
it is the soldier who must suffer and bear the
deepest wounds and scars of war."*
- General Douglas MacArthur (d. 4/5/64)

one of my veteran heroes called me *Babe*
I called him *Baba* – affectionate names a letter
apart
    my step-grandfather, made me feel seen, loved and
safe
    in his gruff raspy voice he'd say *you have to have the
essentials babe*
school shopping at Sears each September-
watching from his two-seat kitchen table,
I'd ask "how do you make the eggs taste so good?"
    he'd instruct *babe, the key is to take them off the heat*

quickly and keep stirring

    we fed ducks in Stonybrook, watched horses graze

for hours in St. James

drank hand-cups of water from a natural spring

watching baseball, he'd teach me good plays while

I colored

    always his fridge stocked to present me with

my favorite lunches

    while he would make for himself a sandwich

with *stinky cheese*

    the modest second floor one-bedroom attic

apartment looked painful to navigate

given his braces; yet he loved to share stories of

the Smithtown Bull and his nightclub singing

    when I got my license, I drove him in his red

and white Chevy to the Veteran's Hospital

    he'd state in a firm low tone *I love you dearly...but you*

must go slow on wet leaves babe

he had waited months and months for each doctor

appointment

and we'd wait hours and hours in a dank cafeteria
for him to be seen

   I first thought he must be exaggerating about
these delays in care
but I witnessed the waits many times over
decades
we hoped for better care when he moved to the
Soldiers home in DC
where despite near blindness setting in,
he could still steer me directions

   to his favorite restaurant, beaming pride to
staff our joyful visits

   when health declined, he was moved to the
veteran's hospital
where he waited and waited and waited for
doctoral care
he tried to fix blankets so I couldn't see his
swollen legs and feet covered in sores

   I am fine; it's ok; nurses will come

No, haven' t seen a doctor in months; It is the

way here; I'm ok.

I felt his pain despite attempts to shield me not just bodily,

but the abandonment and

time lost sitting outside listening to squirrels forage nuts he

threw under fluttering leaves

    his nurse advocate fought for him

    approached hospital administration and

anyone who would listen

I pray his passing was a gentle grace despite

failures of timely care—

trumpets sounded Taps and rifles fired three

volleys

    when I was presented with his flag

    due respect given him in Arlington

like so many who have served

gave their hearts, their peace so we may have ours

    yet is it only in their active service and

    in their death when we truly honor them?

196

About the Author
Sheri Lynn

Once business innovator, now award-winning poet and photographer Sheri Lynn, 2018-2022, was published by: Ms. Magazine, Long Island Quarterly, Chicken Soup for the Soul, Paumanok Transitions (co-editor), NCPLS, PPA, DBP, Bards, TNSPS, 911 Memorial Museum, Odyssey and now LIAG. Sheri launched chapbook "Nature's Breath", accompanying notecards and BreatheInsights.com in 2019

WHERE HAVE ALL THE SOULS GONE

by

Jeff Rimland

My heart is heavy,

from 21 years ago,

with losing you.

Even now,

Russia raising its Soviet head,

In blitzkrieg fashion,

and over the centuries.

Senseless war and death.

Conquests worldwide,in history.

Greeks, Rome, Europe, Africa,

Civil Wars, WWI, and WWII.

Millions upon Millions, upon Millions,

dead.

3 millennium later,

death continues to take all the souls,

leaving a question that hangs on to my psyche.

Where have all the souls gone?

Leading to the ultimate question for me.

Where has your soul gone?

About the Author
Jeff Rimland

Jeff Rimland is an author of 5 books of poetry, possesses an MBA in International Business, taught college business courses, is a board member of the Long Island Author's Group, a member of the prestigious Poets House, and has over 40 years of business experience.

www.longislandauthorsgroup.org

www.poetshouse.org

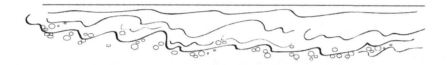

non-fiction

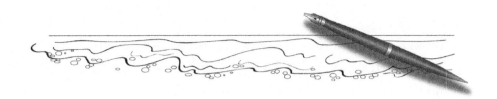

DON'T PROMISE A FRIEND

by

David B. Axelrod

Don't promise to sit with a friend until he dies. He tells me he isn't going to play that stinking cancer game. No poison, no chopping off pieces, no colostomy bags and besides, once it hits your esophagus and your brain, they can't exactly cut it all out. For his part, he refuses to take test after test, so they can't write down a definitive diagnosis. The doctor just takes me aside and says, "Look, you're his health proxy. By now we know 99.9% for sure it's cancer so let him do it his way."

We contact home hospice, and they start us off all smiles and reassurances about death with dignity, and enough "comfort care" that he doesn't need to worry about the pain. I like that euphemism. Comfort care is so much cuter than hard drugs.

VSED stands for Voluntarily Stopping Eating and Drinking. Did you know it's your constitutional right to

205

do that—particularly if you are terminal, but because my friend refuses to get a final diagnosis, his medical charts don't say he has cancer in several places.

When the actual hospice nurse—not the administrator who signed him up—comes to evaluate him, she says, "You know, we won't assist in suicide. The diagnosis is indefinite so you're talking about suicide."

"No," my friend says, "I've always been happy with my life. Now, I know what I need to do, and I'm not afraid of dying." He tells me to take her out on his terrace and show her. I bring her out on this balcony where you can see the ocean and an inland waterway.

"Wow," she says, "What a view."

"Look down," I tell her, encouraging her toward the concrete railing. "Sixteen stories," I tell her. "It only takes three seconds to fall. Five stories is enough to kill you. And you think my friend is suicidal? He could jump anytime."

She leaves saying she's going to discuss Baker Acting my buddy—having him committed because she thinks he is a danger to himself. She thinks he doesn't want to get better.

Now I don't know if I'm going to sit by his bedside until he dies or visit him in the bin while they pump him with antidepressants, as if that would cure him. As if he wouldn't be glad to live longer if that were possible.

But they do send a caregiver to his house—a sincere, ten-buck-an-hour woman who holds my friends arm to help him get up to piss however many times a day.

To assuage the intake nurse who thinks he's suicidal, he consents to taking Lexapro, though he tells me it does about as much good as if he shoved it up his ass. I tell him it is available as a suppository, but I won't be the one to insert it. And I stay for five, six or more hours with him every day.

We have an agreement that I'll tell him such bad jokes that by the time he's really weak, he'll wish he were dead. We go a couple weeks like that before he realizes he doesn't want to linger. It's time to take it to the next step. He stops eating, and for good measure, he barely drinks anything.

It's also time to make "The Arrangements," But the woman who comes to his place to plan the cremation doesn't like our sense of humor. She lists the fancy ways they can reduce him to ashes, and he declines them all.

"We have a Cremation Casket with a white crepe interior, no bed of course. Our price is just $899." She seems sure we will recognize a good deal.

"A sandalwood coffin would smell great," I say.

"You could all sit in the lotus position as I burn," my friend says, "and chant Om."

The cremation specialist doesn't get it. She lists a couple other options, and my friend goes with a cardboard box.

"I'm okay with lying on some wax paper," he says. She declines to say whether that is an option or even legal.

"Do you want the brass urn for your ashes?" She persists, but did she really need to ask?

He goes with a much smaller cardboard box to hold him, and she insists that he specify who will claim his ashes—that being me, the loyal friend.

She prints out the agreement on this neat portable printer and I say, "Hey, you left out the most important option."

"What?" she asks, hopeful she can still pump up her commission.

"Marshmallows and chocolate."

She misses it completely.

"S'mores," my friend tells her, "For when he's there while you burn me."

He signs. She leaves. I'm staying now for something like eight hours a day and worry that I shouldn't leave him with the people that hospice sends because:

A. They don't have a sense of humor either.

B. They waltz in and say, "Can I get you a sandwich," when he's already been fve days without eating and they truly don't understand this VSED, and,

C. Men don't like to use a bedpan, or maybe it's just conditioning, so he thinks he has to stand up to piss, so if the aide leaves the room, he tries to get up to piss and he falls.

He's fallen twice already and has the cuts and bruises to prove it.

"Maybe you can sleep here," he suggests, but he doesn't have a second bed.

"I love you dearly," I tell him, "But you're sure as shit too ugly for me to sleep with you."

Of course, they are screwing with his meds. They don't want him to have narcotics because he might become addicted. Hello? A dying man here? I don't think addiction is a going to be a problem.

How long do you think someone can go without eating? It's been a week. He's not quite Auschwitz but it's getting grotesque. He really hasn't been able to swallow much for months, eating so much egg salad he might as well have feathers.

209

It turns out you can go weeks and weeks without eating much of anything. He decides to go completely without drinking. Dehydration can certainly kill you pretty quickly, except don't promise to sit with a friend until he dies. Or at least consider that having cancer doesn't mean he has a weak heart. His mind might be thinking he's ready to die but his heart has a will of its own.

"Takes a licking and keeps on ticking," only you may not be as old as my friend and I who remember John Cameron Swayze — the first person to broadcast the news on television. "Ladies and gentlemen, a good evening to you. Sit back, light up a Camel and be an eyewitness to the happenings that made history in the last twenty-four hours." For all his puffing as he brought us the news, after his news- casting days, John Cameron Swayze had a long career peddling Timex watch and lived to be 89. My friend is 75. He's out of time but the damn ticker just won't quit.

Twelve days without food and the last five days without a drop to drink, he's still alive, though his urine has gone from blood red to thick coffee.

Did you know even when you don't drink, your body still puts out urine? And did you know that even when a man is debilitated and delirious, he still wants to stand up to piss? I have to climb into his bed and restrain him so he doesn't try to lift himself to the edge of the bed where he's so weak he will fall.

It's all so hard to watch, I'm forgetting to joke. "Did you hear about the fellow who got hit by a car? Someone rushes over and covers him with a sweater. Another fellow rolls up a jacket and puts it under his head and asks, 'are you comfortable?' The man on the ground looks up and says, 'I make a living.'"

I can make the rest of the story go more quickly even though it takes fully seventeen days, the last eight of which are completely without food and liquids. He develops a fever —probably a urinary tract infection. He hits 104. They want to cool him off and give him antibiotics. They still think it's their job to keep him alive.

They informed me a couple days before that they might completely stop sending health aides because he doesn't have a terminal diagnosis on his chart and, "Just dying isn't covered by Medicaid. We might not get reimbursed if we send someone to sit with him just because he's close to death." It's all I can do to get someone to come for the last nights.

I tell him he's done a great job evoking sympathy, not to mention that some people are just dying to be skinny, and he's come up with a sure-fire weight-loss plan.

"You've done what you needed. Just let go." I say,

and I want to believe there is a faint sigh of acknowledgement. "Die," I tell him. "It's getting too melodramatic."

I worry that I am beginning to mean it, but I can't blame him for his last breaths. I'm the fool who promised to sit with my friend until he dies. I could have just encouraged him over the balcony. Instead, I grip his hand firmly as he passes, and the hospice caregiver leaves the room to let me cry.

About the Author
Dr. David B. Axelrod

Dr. David B. Axelrod was Suffolk County, Long Island's and is now Volusia County, Florida's, Poet Laureate (appointed for 2015-2023). For his third Fulbright, he was the first Poet Laureate in the People's Republic of China. His twenty-third book of poetry is *Mother Tongue*. Read more at his website:

www.poetrydoctor.org.

MUD, MISERY AND MUSIC

by

Al Campo

It was the afternoon of August 17, 1969, when Rick
and I had finished walking the 14 miles from Yasgur's
farm to his MG parked on the NYS Thruway. To return to
Long Island we needed to head south and the Route 32
Woodstock exit just slightly north of us was the most
convenient turnaround. But first we had to contend with
the crew-cutted NY State Trooper staring at us through his
reflective silver shades, in his form fitting tan shirt
adorned with the glistening golden badge affixed above
his left breast pocket, dark black belt with a holstered 38
pistol, tan bloused pants and riding boots, he stood beside
his cruiser that blocked the exit ramp.

He approached us after we came to a stop, advising us
that the exit was closed, and we would have to travel
another eleven miles north to the Catskill exit in order to
turn back.

We pleaded with the officer attempting to have him

see how illogical it was for us to travel eleven miles in order to reverse direction when we could simply do it right there. We explained that we were just trying to get home and had no intention of heading back to Woodstock.

The shadows of sweat on his light tan shirt evidenced his discomfort standing in the hot sun, so we thought we would offer him some libation to quench his thirst. In the back of Rick's two-seater was a cooler containing the only supplies we thought of taking with us for the long weekend. I reached back into the cooler and offered the officer a can of Schaefer beer to quench his thirst, and he surprisingly accepted our tribute. The hot sun of the previous day had performed its magic. It succeeded in converting the little ice that was in the Styrofoam cooler to tepid water as well as heat up the beer. Imagine his embarrassment and our sense of panic when after snapping open the pop top his meticulously ironed shirt became a blotter for the splattered beer spewing from the can. I thought he was going to shoot us.

With a curled lip, he tilted his head brushing his shirt with the back of his hand. Rather than drag the encounter out any longer he conceded to let us pass. The stout officer turned his body like a matador evading a bull, and pointed both arms while still holding the beer, and told us to get the hell out of there.

That would be the final leg of my three-day

experience at Woodstock. What was billed as three days of Peace, Love and Music for me was more like to three days of Mud, Misery, and some Music.

It all started that Friday night of the concert when my friends George Ulrich, Rick Triola, Willie and Richie Tammone and I were slurping down beers at Howie Chatterton's Bar and Grill. News of the concert appeared on the television behind the bar and that planted the seed of spontaneity. We decided that we would travel to Saugerties, NY and attend the festival. Mapping out our plan we pooled our limited resources and purchased four cases of beer, a couple of Styrofoam coolers, some ice, gathered several blankets piled into the two cars and at about 11:00 PM headed upstate. George rode shotgun for Rick. I rode with the twins in the back seat of Richie's mustang.

The two vehicles sped up the NY Thruway never losing sight of each other. Then it began to rain when we reached Dobbs Ferry. By the time we reached the Tappan Zee Bridge the wet pavement reflected the parkway lights like a glistening row of pearls off the paved surface. Luckily, we were the only two cars crossing the bridge at that hour because suddenly Rich's car began to spin out of control. He succeeded in regaining control of the car after completing one full 360. The trip was off to an inauspicious start.

217

We arrived at the Saugerties exit just before dawn. Since police had closed the exit, we parked both vehicles on the shoulder of the thruway along with the hundreds of other cars already there. Most of the beer had been consumed before and during the drive to the festival, so we grabbed the blankets and proceeded to walk to Yasgur's farm. During that period in my life, the son of a cop, although at times rebellious, I was a conservative guy. However, I decided to let what short hair I had down and elected to go barefoot for the weekend. That would later prove to be a poor decision on my part.

The sun began to breach the horizon soon after we reached Route 212 where we joined the caravan of characters heading to the concert. Richie broke off from our group for a short time and managed to hook back up with us about a half hour later, carrying a plastic bag containing what he said was marijuana. As I said, I was pretty conservative, and had never seen or indulged in the herb. I was also shocked to discover that my friend, whom I thought I knew quite well, smoked pot. We walked for what seemed like hours and miles and during our trek spotted some peculiar characters. The oddest being a tall, bearded, sinewy, gray-haired man who was carrying a sheep in his arms. That was the only thing adorning his body.

Rich wanted to stop and sample the dope he bought.

218

So, we got off the road and draped a gray woolen blanket over a cable attached to a telephone pole as support. The five of us took cover under the blanket and Rich proceeded to roll a joint. Suddenly the sky opened, and a torrent of rain poured down upon us. While we passed the joint around, the woolen blanket weighted by the water was now saturated. It began to slowly enfold us. We must have looked like a clay statue of five huddled bodies to those passing by. We took advantage of what little protection that wet blanket provided, but it didn't take long for the entire party to become as sodden as that blanket and we crawled out from under it as soon as the rain ended about a half hour later. We wrung out as much water as we could from the blanket as well as our clothes and proceeded on our way.

We asked a local resident every fifteen to thirty minutes how much farther it was to the event and received the same "about two miles" down the road response. I began to feel the need to eat by the time we reached the tiny burgh of Woodstock. The main thoroughfare through the town was bordered on both sides by old plank colonial homes, a gas station, a hardware store and a deli that was selling a quarter pound of ham for $1. Needing to conserve what little money I had, I purchase $1 worth of ham and ate it sans bread. It was about that time that we encountered Timmy Atz another fellow Lindenhurst resident and classmate.

Another two miles and another two miles and another two miles down the road when we finally reached our destination. By that time the wave of people had collapsed the fences and entry into the concert was gratis. This was fortunate considering my scant money supply.

We approached the crest of the hillside and looked down upon a sea of people. All were focused on the giant stage in front of them. Scaffolds holding spotlights were adjacent to each side of the stage. Trailers and tents dotted the land behind the staging area. My group sat down at the top of the hill and began to enjoy the show. Santana was on stage finishing up his song "Persuasion". Fatigued from all the walking, I fell asleep on the mixture of wet grass and orange mud, and when I awoke Rick, George, Rich and Willie were gone and I had managed to sleep through the rest of Santana's set and part of the Incredible String Band's as well.

A sense of dread pervaded my consciousness, "How in hell am I going to find these guys in this immense crowd? If I can't find them how the hell am I going to get home?" My mouth now had that remnant dryness of a hangover, and I desperately needed to hydrate. I looked around and saw the concession stand about seventy-five yards from where I sat. I rolled over and used my arms and knees to stand erect. I crashed down to the ground as

220

both feet were struck with intense pain. Looking at my feet, I could see both were crimson red and so swollen they looked like two pork butts attached to my ankles. But I was thirsty and needed water. I tried to stand again and failed. Left with one alternative and in dire need of water, I crawled on my hands and knees to the concession stand, grunting all the way. It must have been a curious spectacle for those watching me. Then again, they probably thought I was tripping on acid. I reached the concession stand and stood up long enough to order and pay for a bottle of water. I gulped it and crawled back to what would be considered my seat at the venue.

The balance of the afternoon was hazy to me and hard to recall. I did however manage to find Richie who said that he had met Helen McGowan, a recent graduate of Lindenhurst High School. Helen and her friends were older, much smarter, and better prepared than my companions, because they had tents and sleeping bags! They had camped across the road that ran along the periphery of the field and down the embankment in a small clearing.

They also had drugs. Not the illegal kind but one that I was in desperate need of. Richie and I joined Helen's group and traded stories of the weekend. I began sweating profusely. Helen noticed and placed her hand on my forehead and realized I was afire with fever. She must have been a girl scout when she was younger, because she was prepared for everything. She had the two things that I needed most at that time sleep, and aspirins. I swallowed the aspirins and accepted her offer to let me sleep in her tent.

And sleep I did. Apparently, I slept through most of the concert since it was nearly 6:00 PM Saturday evening when I crawled into her tent. When I awoke, Rickie was at Helen's campsite, so I at least had a ride home. Beyond that I have only a vague recollection of buying the iconic Woodstock poster. We left the farm to get Rick's car while listening to Jimi Hendrix's version of the "Star-Spangled Banner" in the distance. That was Monday afternoon, the end of my "Woodstock" experience.

About the Author
Al Campo

Born April 18, 1950, Al Campo is a retired mortgage banker who graduated from Lindenhurst High School in 1968. After attending the University of Missouri, he honorably served in the US Navy. His historical fiction, The Funny Thing About War furnishes a sailor's perspective of the Vietnam War.

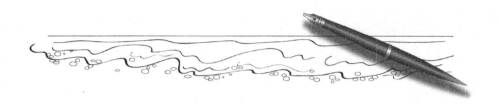

THE MOST OFTEN ASKED QUESTION:

How Did the Long Island Authors Group Get Started?

by

John P. Cardonc

It has been said that the Beatles have done more for popular music than any other modern musical group. Any review of their accomplishments would indicate that they are the most successful recording act of all time. In addition to selling more than one billion albums world-wide, many of today's performers will say they were influenced in some way by the Beatles. Well, you might not believe this—but the Beatles also influenced the founding of the Long Island Authors Group.

It was the summer of 2007: my wife Kathy and I had been cycling on the North Fork of Long Island as we frequently do. On the way back, driving along Sound Avenue, just West of CR 48 in Mattituck, we decided to

225

make a stop at Martha Clara Vineyards (now RGNY Wine).

There was a sign out front indicating a special event, a Beatles Art Show and it caught my attention. After completing a wine tasting, we asked about the Beatles Art Show and were directed to the Winery's Event Pavilion next door. It was an interesting exhibit of candid Beatle's photos, album cover art, and assorted posters. We strolled along the exhibit checking out the art while listening to Beatle's music on the overhead sound system.

Somewhere along the back tables, as I watched the crowd circulating it hit me – what a wonderful building for an art event and what a great venue to draw a crowd. Now around the same time I had recently self-published my first book, a medical murder mystery entitled, Without Consent and was looking for new ways (actually, any way) to market it. I started thinking, maybe I could have a signing here – and I quickly realized, maybe there should be other authors to attract attention. The question entered my mind, would Martha Clara be willing to host a group of authors—a sort of book fair featuring Long Island authors? Why not I thought on the drive home, after all, authors fall into the art category —people like to meet authors, and the idea of featuring local Long Island authors would be an interesting draw.

As the days went on, I couldn't shake the notion that

226

the author event I had thought of might just work. I prepared a simple to-do-list, writing down the obvious things to start the ball rolling. At the top of the list, was contacting the Winery — after all, without a venue there could be no event. I looked up Martha Clara Vineyards on the Internet and using their contact us page made a note of their phone number. One day, holding my breath, I picked up the phone and made the call. I asked to speak with the person who coordinates winery events – it turned out her name was Keri McKillop. I explained my idea to Keri, and she greeted it with enthusiasm explaining that Martha Clara Vineyards, a winery owned by the Entenmann family, welcomed events that featured the arts. We talked about how the author event might work and agreed to follow up in another month or so. As I hung up the phone smiling, I looked at the next item on my to-do-list, contact local authors; the smile fell off my face.

In my spare time, over the next days and weeks, I worked on several Google searches for LI authors using different key words and search strings. The results netted a handful of book titles and author names. At first, my hand- written list of authors was random – a sort of first come, first listed approach. Then, as I learned of the Book titles, I started to organize the books into standard book categories. More searches of the author's names resulted in several websites, and many of these had contact the author e-mail links. Among the first authors I contacted was Kerriann Flanagan Brosky, author of Ghosts of Long Island. The contact information on her website was through her publicist, and I thought at the very best, reaching Kerriann was a long shot.

I also contacted Robert Muller, author of Long Island Lighthouses: Past & Present. Both Robert and Kerriann symbolized the idea of LI Authors in my mind—authors who lived on LI and wrote about it. However, this caused a huge problem because that idea didn't include me. So, I modified the idea, authors who lived on LI, wrote about LI or told a story that took place on LI.

In addition to Web searches, I also visited several bookstores in Suffolk County. These included, The Book Revue in Huntington, Book Hampton, Borders Books & Music in Stony Brook and Runaway Books in Sayville (sadly, except for Book Hampton, all the other stores have closed). In each of these stores, I inquired if they had a section devoted to Long Island authors. Some stores had no special section, others lumped local authors into a section that was geographically based. So, next to books on New York City, Cape Cod, and Las Vegas were books about Long Island. Typically, I was directed to either a small table or a shelf in a remote area of the store. Thinking about how I planned to feature Long Island Authors, this did not bode well for my plans.

In the Book Revue I picked up a book that I knew immediately would have to be included in the plans for a Long Island Authors Book Fair – the title was Jones Beach, and the author was John Hanc. Later, I learned that John Hanc did freelance writing for LI Newsday and had a special interest in writing about sports and LI. I added John to the contact list. In Book Hampton, I picked up one of the largest and heaviest books. It was also one of the most beautiful books anyone could own. The authors were Anne Surchin and Gary Lawrence, and the book is titled, Houses of the Hamptons: I laughed at the idea that if we were to have a book about Jones Beach, on the other side of the historical and social spectrum, we also would have to have a book about the Hamptons.

One day, I went to visit the Runaway Book Store in Sayville. I introduced myself to the owner Marianne Bastian and after we got to talking about LI Authors and she showed me to a table in the middle of the store that had a number of books by LI Authors. She asked me, "Do you know David Axelrod?" "No, I replied," as she handed me one of his books. Maryanne explained that David was a poet, an educator, and one of those people who spends a lot of time helping writers. I wrote his name down along-side a couple of his poetry book titles. It turned out when I Googled David – that at the time he was the Suffolk County Poet Laureate. I thought to myself, this is too good to be true – what would a book fair be without the Suffolk County Poet Laureate?

At this point, I had a pretty good list of authors – authors of books that would draw attention and fit the bill for a Long Island Book Fair. I pressed forward contacting each author by e-mail or phone. When I composed those e-mails I focused on the planned Book Fair at Martha Clara, but also indicated this event would be a great way to meet other authors. Interestingly, it was this idea that seemed to plant a seed among the participants. Across the board, everyone looked forward to meeting fellow authors and comparing notes. One of the things I like to explain about this is the simple fact that while most writers tend to be lone wolves, joining this group of authors meant they could also become part of a pack.

The responses started to come in – at first there were questions... what would the event cost? How would it be publicized? Who would be there? What is the name of the organization putting the event together? These were all good questions – it was the last one that made me stop and think?

Yes, we needed an official group title. Sometimes after the initial e-mails, I had phone conversations with the perspective book fair participants. In one case, when I was asked again about the name of the organization – I looked down at my notes and there centered above the author's names was the heading, LI Authors... and that's what I used as the official name—Long Island Authors, I explained.

By this time, Winter was just starting to roar. Over these weeks, I had many conversations with Keri McKillop from Martha Clara. I reported the number of participating LI Authors were approaching sixteen and that there was a great deal of enthusiasm. Somewhere along the line, we took out our calendars and decided on a date for the event – Sunday, March 9th from noon to 4 pm. One of the participating authors, Florence Gatto, promised me sun; weather was a big fear and something no one could control. If there was a storm it would stop people from traveling.

When speaking about this event, I tried to sell the idea that the book fair would be a festive way to promote reading and writing on Long Island. To help this along, I thought it would great to connect with the libraries and with the LI Writer's Guild. If these organizations could help with promotion, then we would have a better focus on reading and writing. The Boards of both groups voted unanimously to join in. I felt we were heading in the right direction.

It was now around the middle of the winter and spring was fast approaching. The next major task was promotion. This would not be easy since we had no major financial backing, no money to speak of, and no public relations network to use. It is times like these when you turn to your friends. I had two special friends that I went to. One was a long-time family friend, and a very talented artist named Rosa Patterson. The other was a business contact of mine; a family run printing business in Ronkonkoma called St. James Printing operated by Gert & Paula Kuehnel.

Rosa asked me what the budget was? I had to tell her we didn't have a budget and that I would have to pay for her work. As I mentioned, I knew Rosa a very long time, so she offered to do the work for free, but I felt awful about that. Instead, she provided the art services at a very low, very affordable rate. We decided to create an event flyer that could be enlarged and used as a poster. I asked Rosa to design the flyer to include the names of the authors participating along-side their book covers. It was the book covers that drew attention—they were Long Island. It took a great deal of hard work to quickly pull together the items needed such as the correct titles, book covers from the authors in usable digital formats, and frankly, I think I drove Rosa a little crazy with all the e-mails. Gert and Paula offered to print the flyers and posters at a special discount rate. It was amazing to me that so many people liked the idea of the authors group and offered to help. It was a very positive feeling that something good was coming from this idea.

So, there we were, the Long Island Authors Group was formed. We had a venue, a date, and sixteen authors willing to spend a Sunday promoting reading and writing along-side the Suffolk County Library Association and the LI Writer's Guild. We had our flyers and our posters printed. Newsday ran a big story about the event as did Suffolk Life. There were more phone calls and e-mails asking for more information. The Suffolk County Library Association and the LI Writer's Guild promoted the event helping us get the word out.

March 9, 2008 arrived and the authors set up their tables —all wondering what the day would bring. Members of the Suffolk County Library Association and the Writer's Guild put their tables together as we all watched for the visitors. One of the things I like to mention about this very first event at Martha Clara was the simple fact that as the day went on and the crowd grew, two things went up—the room noise and our book sales. I still don't know if it was the festive atmosphere, the book titles, or the wine. Perhaps it was all three. The number of visitors was estimated to be between three and four hundred people, most of them book lovers. During the event, the authors asked about the next event and what was next? There was a great deal of excitement about this event and the group of authors who banded together to form that pack. And that's how it started; the Long Island Authors Group was born. Started up in the late months of 2007 and officially established with a Board of Directors in 2008. There you have it, thanks in part, to the Beatles. I still hear the music & the lyrics by John Lennon to, "Imagine."

About the Author
John P. Cardone

LIAG Founder & President Emeritus

John P. Cardone retired in December 2018 after 40 years as a writer/producer of patient education, medical education, and health promotion videos and interactive media programs. These days, he actively spends his time inspiring people to get outdoors with nature. John is an author, a nature photographer, a wildlife photography instructor, and a lecturer on nature topics. He grew up in Astoria, NY moving to Long Island after his military service in 1970. John is proud to say he is the founder of the Long Island Authors Group and a two-time cancer survivor. To learn more about John, his books, and his nature work, visit: www.WaterviewsBook.com

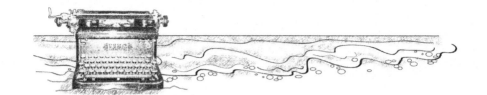

BAG OF FAITH

by

Vincent Casale

There is one certainty I will stand by. Life, my friends, is truly uncertain. January 2019, I was planning a trip to South Florida. I finally managed to secure a more than reasonable air fare. OK, I booked it. The hotel, since I was a regular customer, also came with a nice discount. I was set. The New York winters are starting to wear on my sixty-year-old bones, so I was psyched for this trip. South Florida has become the new mecca for aging adults because there is always something different to do, especially if you're looking to night crawl after a day of sun-tanning. I am retired so I'm up for both.

Morning, at work, a security job, not too exciting, me and my boss laughing about the drudgery of the court system, it's foolish delays and attempted bargains. We are talking of divorce court, by the way. Suddenly they come, like an unexpected swipe at the gut. Pains, abominable pains one wishes would end before they begin. Then they get worse, the swipe a full-blown punch.

Pain, I haven't felt in any un-natural way since my kidney stone.

"Buddy," I said to my boss. "I'm feeling very intense stomach pains." I press slightly on my belly. My boss sensing urgency decides to call an ambulance.

"No ambulance...I could make it to Huntington Hospital."

"But you're doubling over," he said.

"It's fine, I'll call you when I'm there..."

Next thing, my pants are off, the stupid backwards gown is half on, and there are two nurses urging me to calm down. They are getting ready to push a catheter into my penis; my eyes go wide, and I scream,

"You put that damn thing inside me I will rip it out and the hell with you."

"Sir, sir," they mumble, almost simultaneously. "You cannot do such a thing, there will be blood everywhere."

"I don't care, I do not want that pain on top of the agony I am currently feeling."

I am like a fish out of water, and I wiggle to no end.

Unable to sit still, the pain is so severe. I could care less now if they put me out of my misery by any means possible. One of the nurses feeds me a pain killer. I succumb to the catheter. I reiterate between clenched teeth that "It just isn't gonna' work."

Fast forward, more pain killers, it is not the prostate, rather diverticulitis getting worse by the minute. A tall mature specialist is over me patting my arm, "Sir, you need surgery, and..." blah, blah." I don't want to listen to him. I hear colostomy. I hear Sepsis. "No surgery," I state. "No, no, no. Got it."

As patients in this country, we have that right.

On Good Friday, the day Jesus was crucified, a friend asked me to go to the local church and view the reenactment, the stations of the cross as told in the Catholic faith. Since my unexpected surgery, I have lost some of what little faith I've had to begin with, as I am one of those who question God's plan when there is so much pain in the world, especially my pain.

"If anything," my friend said, "you will, I think, enjoy the reenactment as a sort of mini play."

The church was as suspected very crowded, which is usually the case on holy days such as Good Friday. I watched as the players in the production began the roles of Christ, his followers, and the Roman executioners.

I was struck by the beginning verse of the production, "Abba, Abba, I put my life in your hands." Abba is Father, the almighty.

Now I'm not pretending to be a religious fanatic, nor did I suddenly have an epiphany, but I reflected, as a reasonable man, not only did I almost die, but since feeling wounded, I have been realizing a sense of empathy.

"Did you ever think you would be here on a Friday night?" my friend whispered.

"Of course not, I would be at happy hour somewhere in previous years. If you and I didn't speak today I would not have been here." He wouldn't have been here either if not for his newfound sobriety.

I was paying deep attention to the re-enactment. Christ truly suffered unbearable grief and pain so who was I to question my own sickness? Yes, I had needles stationed in both arms and was pinched daily, but the Lord went through a lot worse. I really thought about this.

For once in my life learn a little gratitude. Yes, I caught some bum breaks, but I did not have cancer and such a fact is so huge. My father died at my age, stomach cancer. Two years of unbearable suffering. So, for a moment in that church I was profoundly ready to accept the grace of God and I was going to heal soon and move

240

on.

I left Huntington Hospital a different man than when I entered. I was going home minus seven inches of colon and fitted with a colostomy bag, which would collect my business, number two, for the next six months. I would grow accustomed to new habits, social interaction, sleep positions, eating schedule, etc.

During my hospital stay, the little tan bag had broken in my sleep a few times, causing a nauseating mess likened to rotten gasses. I was deeply humiliated, but the nurse staff at the hospital was tremendous in their empathy and duty, not one creating the phony, miserable, hiding smile.

"Please Vincent, do not be embarrassed," one young nurse said. "This is why we are here." another said, as she gathered up the soiled sheets.

Why aren't they wearing at least masks to protect them from the stench? They were used to it.

So, they fed me, took my vitals, comforted me, changed my bag, adjusted my intravenous, and tucked me in. All the while shuffling along from bed to bed attending to other patients. A dedicated nurse is a true angel. They even showered me, where at first, I felt like an invalid. Of course, the hospital staff was quite gentle, but I never had to be washed and hosed down before. After two and a half weeks I was scared to leave the hospital.

There were still stitches that weren't exactly in a straight line from belly to crotch. It was a wound still draining and, along with the beginning of stoma care, I would have to be attended by a visiting nurse. Like a funeral when the mourners stop coming, the surgery hit me hard. I was alone now, no visitors, only my elderly mother eager to do what she could, bless her.

Every once in a while, she would boost my confidence by reiterating, "Son, not only are you going to be OK, but you are taking it better than we all thought."

My head swimming with thoughts, of the past and the present. As far as the future, who knew, I was mortal now. A year ago, drinking four nights a week and smoking two packs a of cigarettes a day, now could I die at any second? The mind is as fragile as the body in the long run. Negativity can engulf us to believe the worst is not over, and by the way "Your life was a failure...mistakes...apologies not cutting it."

Now I could see of the quote, "Don't judge until you walked in my shoes."

Everyone I knew would reiterate in sincere kind, "The worst is over. You will get used to it and eventually you will heal...you are stronger than you think."

One friend joked, "Look at me, I'm bald, you have hair at least."

Though these are words meant in earnest they cannot be rendered heartfelt. If you haven't walked in my shoes.... Did they really believe I would get used to wearing a colostomy bag on my stomach? Believe me, I tried, I had no choice. I was out and about but all the while conscious of my protruding left side, the elephant in every room I entered. The ownership of an extra body part, complete with its own odor. I have sat next to people at dinners and meetings, aware of a warm flow that would fill the pouch, sometimes an acute smell rising from under my shirt. I had to believe, and hope, those around me didn't have any idea what the heck I was feeling.

Gratefulness never came easy for me but it's never too late to learn. I have met people who have really been sick. Some who must wear the faith bag for life, showing that God does in fact make some sacred and resilient folks, bless them. It's amazing to witness those who take adversity and morph it into a productive life.

At a hospital support meeting one such guy, a life -long colostomy wearer, a man in his fifties with life changing Crohn's disease, was patting my back, comforting my complaints, I couldn't believe it.

"Don't worry, my friend," he said. "You will be fine I

promise you. There's always someone to talk to you and help you."

For me, in the early going, it was the poor me. "What the...I won't...I can't...Who will ever want to be with me? ...Poor divorced, drama filled, bag wearing me?"

How completely selfish to be so ungrateful, to the doctors, and whatever higher power there is. Yes, I wore a colostomy bag. Yes, I had to act as protector, often palming the pouch like a puppy, assuring it wouldn't jump out of my hand. I learned to quiet the icky meter having had to be in close nose and hand contact with the unknown. I even worried about the clothes I wore. But again, truth be told, without the bag I certainly could have died, plain and simple.

On that Good Friday, parishioners, from different walks of life, went to the standing cross just to touch it, say a prayer in front of it. The elderly, the young, the sick, black, white, families, all with one goal, to pray for good on this ultimate day of suffering.

How life changes. As I prayed and remembered my life over these last years. Can there be forgiveness and faith? "I've made mistakes, but I'm not a bad person...If you never speak to me again, please forgive me, and my judgements... please love me."

Humility, I wanted terribly to enter the threshold of

244

humanity. "Help, please, somebody." My God I heard his suffering, and I knew it well. Faint whispers and cries,

"Help, oh Mom, help."

If I had been in the hospital for a less afflicting ailment, the train wreck syndrome which cause humans to nervously laugh, might have gotten a chuckle out of me. I mean a seventy-year-old man moaning for his mother. But I knew that man behind the curtain, in the next bed, was indeed hurting.

I was once again hampered with abdominal pain, even as my new reversal surgery was a success, even as I was loaded up with various pain killers from a grueling five-hour second surgery. I was readying for my walk around the corridor, gripping the medicine bag pole, but frst passed my roommate still fat on his back after suffering a ruptured ulcer.

"How are you, my friend?"

"I'm OK," he replied. "But how are you?"

"I'm better and I hear you, I know how you feel," I said. "There is no pain like stomach pain."

Around 3:00 AM on my last night in Hotel Hospital, I was visited by a male nurse for my last vital and blood test. At first, I was startled as his approaching movement woke me. The light from the moon was shining behind his

245

dreadlocks. I do not believe in God moments but for some reason I thought it strange, his comments.

"I wish you well, my friend," he said. "I don't want to see you back here. No sense with these stomach problems and grief. Take care of yourself and more importantly take care of you...it's your life now, live it for you and not others, enjoy it for you...the past is the past, no more hospital."

What? How did this guy know about my life? How did he know my personal estrangements? I asked him.

"I don't know, sir," he smiled. I just see too many people come in and out of here."

Well, if it weren't a God moment, I had to believe it was some sort of inspiration. Even after two surgeries and a total of twenty-one days in the hospital, not to mention months and months of just lying around in discomfort, how in good faith could I complain. I was going home bag free and more importantly Cancer free.

I explained to my thoughtful daughter what a remarkable operation I just had. My surgeon was aces. Really. A great bed side manner to go along with a wonderful reputation. His hands, skill, and concentration for five hours, was I'm sure no easy task. "It looked like spaghetti in there," he told me. Geez.

"You know what I wish, honey? I don't want to become cocky... I don't want to forget what happened and how I felt...I don't want to be a person who doesn't care about this or that...I want to remember how humbling this whole thing was for me...I want to be empathetic and grateful and know what's important and weed out the rest."

I didn't want to say, but I wanted to move on from the memory of our broken family. I admitted my new theory probably might not work at times. It's a learning process.

My daughter smiled, her face exuding innocence, a young life not yet scarred by living. But she confidently, said, "Dad, there is no reason why that cannot happen."

About the Author
Vincent Casale

Vincent Casale was born in East Harlem, New York City and was raised in Flushing, Queens. In 1984, he took and passed the entry test to become a proud member of the New York City Police Department. A life-long New Yorker, Vincent retired to South Florida in 2019 and is currently writing, blogging, and podcasting.

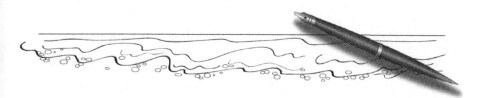

HE GOT A TICKET TO RIDE
(THE WAVES)

by

Thomas M. Cassidy

When the summer season in Long Beach moves into full swing, I hope surfers have as much fun as I did when I rode the waves in the 1960s. Most of my friends back then were city kids who vacationed at the "City by the Sea." We swam, body-surfed and watched the few teenagers who had surfboards with envy. They entertained us for hours at a time in the early morning and evening when the lifeguards were off duty. We laughed when they fell (wipeout) or if the nose of the surfboard sunk and they slid off the front of the board (pearl). If they had a great ride and cut the curl, we cheered. I dreamed every night about getting my chance to ride waves on my own surfboard even though I had no money. But then my luck changed, and I became a Long Beach surfer. Let me explain:

251

Saint Ignatius Martyr Church in Long Beach had their annual bazaar at the beach in 1964. The grand raffle prize was a custom-made red Rick Surfboard with a racing-stripe down the middle. I watched as many of the experienced surfers emptied their wallets and bought tickets for the raffle as I played carnival games with my friends. A few minutes before my nine o'clock curfew, my brother John and I were broke. We gazed at the surfboard again before we left for home. We were disappointed and gloomy because we didn't even take one chance. We pleaded with our older brother Hugh to help us. Hughie grudgingly dug into his wallet, took out a dollar and bought three chances. Then we raced home.

The next morning we got the most exciting phone call ever. We won the best surfboard on Long Island! But not everyone shared our joy. Many skilled surfers who invested most of their money buying raffle tickets hoped one of them would win the prized surfboard. Not an annoying beginner, whom they would call a gremmy (slang for gremlin). But for them the result was even worse, because my brothers and I were totally inexperienced and had not even reached the gremmy level. Never deterred, my brother John and I surfed every minute we could until the day we returned to our home in Stuyvesant Town. Then, to the utter amazement of my classmates at Cardinal Hayes High School in the Bronx I revealed that yes, I am a surfer!

Although we kept our surfboard when my family was uprooted and moved to Stony Brook in my senior year of high school, I rarely trekked to the ocean beaches. Still, our Rick Surfboard was carefully hung from the ceiling of my parent's garage for decades. Many friends asked if they could buy it, and even promised that they would display it proudly in their home or business. The answer was always no. Today, my brother John keeps our surfboard safely in his Long Island home. We both agree that it will not be sold in our lifetimes.

Nevertheless, the thrill of catching waves in Long Beach has resonated as a highpoint throughout my life. So, it was only natural that I include a surfing story in my Manhattan South mysteries. Here's a brief excerpt:

"Donnellan thinks back to September of 1965 when Hurricane Betsy, a powerful Category 4 hurricane was raging deep into the North Atlantic Ocean. Although Betsy stayed far out in the ocean, the intense storm generated massive waves along the shores of east coast beaches. GQ and Donnellan watched as reporters warned that beaches were closed due to the dangerous conditions caused by gigantic waves.

They couldn't sit still. They wanted to get a piece of this historic action. They took the Long Island Railroad to

Long Beach, borrowed a couple of surfboards from their classmate, Brendon O'Reilly, and walked down Delaware Avenue to the beach. They stood there in awe for a full twenty minutes; staring at the waves, listening to the thundering roar, and feeling the wet salt air. They watched the futile struggle of surfers in the water, none of whom could get past the breakers. When a surfer got close, a wave would crush down, and an explosion of whitewater would push them back to the shore.

GQ looked at Donnellan, nodded his head and said, "Let the games begin." The two high school swimmers were faster than the other surfers. They paddled furiously into the heart of the ocean. When a wave crashed and rumbled toward them, they swiftly flipped the board over while holding down the nose and gripping the board with their legs to slow down the momentum, doing what the surfers called a turtle roll. It took forty-five minutes, but they made it past the breakers."

About the Author
Thomas M. Cassidy

Thomas M. Cassidy, a member of the Long Island Authors Group, is the writer and creator of Manhattan South, a TV series that is peppered with the culture, sounds and dialogue of 1980s New York City.

ESSAY

by

Tom Clavin

Every so often I am asked, "How does it feel to be a famous writer?" Usually, an awkward silence follows. By answering directly, I am acknowledging that I am a famous writer. What is "famous?" I begin to ponder. Do more people recognize my name on a book cover than 10 years ago? Yes . . . but so what? I seem to be working at least twice as hard as I did 10 years ago. At least I'm getting paid more for it, which encourages me to believe I'll be able to retire by 80.

But going around thinking that one is famous, what good does that do? Probably more harm, I would think. And anyway, it's not like I'm Tik Tok famous, which is what really counts today.

By this time, the person who posed the question has drifted away, after debating if I've had a stroke and should a doctor be called.

What fame really means to me is that more people are going to see the errors. At least once a week I hear from a reader in Nebraska or Utah or Maryland who questions a piece of information in one of my books or discovers an actual error. One reader pointed out that in my book Wild Bill, I report the fourth child in the Hickok family was born in 1832 and the third child was born in 1834. Mistakes can no longer hide behind obscurity.

Another one: In The Heart of Everything That Is, Bob Drury and I write about Lt. Casper Collins and his death during a battle with Sioux Indians. To honor his heroism, the Wyoming state capital, Casper, was named after him. The manuscript went through countless hours of editing and proofreading before Heart was published and it remains our best-selling book (though the most recent one, Blood and Treasure, is making a run for it). However, it was only after publication that a reader revealed to us that the capital of Wyoming is Cheyenne.

In Lightning Down, published last year, I have the lead character and his fellow pilots embarking from Boston in early 1944 on a ship that sails west to England. That must have been some rough going.

I have learned that the word "famous" is rather meaningless and most important is to keep one's ego right where it was. I was reminded of this a couple of years ago while on Ebay. I stumbled upon someone offering to sell a copy of another Drury/Clavin book, Halsey's Typhoon, for $150 and that it was "signed by both authors." My chest puffed out. I scrolled down. There was an offer to sell another copy of that same book "signed by Bob Drury" for $250.

Four years ago, in San Francisco I was waiting to give a talk and a woman seated in the front row commented on what a great character Jack Ryan was. I politely agreed. "How did you come to create the Ryan character?" Confused, I said, "I didn't." Then it dawned on her. Irritably, she asked, "You're not Tom Clancy?" "No, I'm Tom Clavin." In a huff, she got up and left – before I could add that Clancy had died in 2013 and so far, only my self-esteem was dying.

Probably my crowning achievement in being famous occurred a few summers ago. When my partner, Leslie, and I arrived at the pond-front house in East Hampton that Saturday night, a tipoff should have been that everyone else wore a dinner jacket and I was the only one wearing sneakers. They were pretty nice sneakers, Keds-like, but still: Something wasn't quite right.

The setting, however, could not have been more right. We were standing on the back deck of a house that looked out at Georgica Pond. The evening sky was clear, and

259

with the sun having set about 10 minutes earlier, the western horizon above the pond featured layers of pink and purple. The temperature was perfect and there was barely a breeze. Two swans drifted silently south on the water. But something was off. Maybe a jacket would do the trick. I'd forgotten mine in the car. Leslie found where the valets had parked it and she retrieved the jacket, but even after I slipped my arms into it, we still felt oddly out of place.

Let me backtrack. The "Authors Night" benefit, the annual major fundraiser for the East Hampton Library, had been that afternoon. I've enjoyed participating ever since I was first asked to, in 2007. It's not unusual that I am called "prolific," and people may think I write books with regularity because of the money, or I don't know how to do anything else. Actually, both are true. But I'm kind of a needy and insecure guy, and I figure if I keep producing books, I'll continue to be invited to do book-related benefits and appearances. (Certainly, my looks or personality won't get me there.) Libraries have been especially welcoming.

Anyway, the cocktail reception under a tent in a farm feld that began late that Saturday afternoon was especially enjoyable. As usual, the organizers were gracious. There were lots of book-buyers, but the activity never felt overwhelming. It is fun to encounter new and familiar attendees who so obviously love books and, let's face it, they ensure that I can continue to make a living. Once again, I was seated next to Dick Cavett, whose charm and courtesy are inspiring, and I was able to schmooze a bit with fellow authors Lynn Scherr, Nelson DeMille, Lee Child, and Edward Burns, who easily had the distinction this year of the longest line of people waiting to buy his book, Independent Ed. (I'm sure it was all about the book.)

As the party wound down, the plan was that we were to head to the home of "Jane Smith," who was hosting the dinner at which Carl Safina, with his wonderful new book, Beyond Words: What Animals Think and Feel, and I would be the featured authors. I hadn't previously secured directions, but during the reception Jane Smith had been nice enough to introduce herself and had told me how to get to her house. I checked with Carl that we would rendezvous there, and Leslie and I headed for our car.

I'd been instructed to follow Lily Pond Lane until it ended at Apaquogue Road and turn there. I was to look for white balloons festooned at the end of the driveway. At the end of Lily Pond, I turned left. I did not see balloons white or otherwise, but I did find two teenagers in crisp white shirts who were obviously parking cars for arriving guests. I called out the window that we were here for the book party and they pointed to the second driveway and then a spot to pull into.

We hiked across a lushly landscaped yard toward the back deck and the water. There were 16 people chatting, drinking, and scooping up the passed appetizers. I didn't see our host and apparently Carl Safina had not yet arrived. Even after I slipped my jacket on (nothing could be done about the sneakers), we were ignored by the rather formal gathering. This too was strange because I still had dangling from around my neck the badge that introduced me and that I was an "Authors Night" co-chair. Surely, such a lofty position entitled me to a handshake at least, but we seemed to be invisible to everyone except the catering staff. On the deck a table was elegantly set for dinner. I figured we'll eat and leave, and I'll ask for a more courteous and accommodating gathering next year.

As dark took hold, a well-dressed woman emerged from the house and announced it was time for dinner. The guests looked for their name cards, and I wondered if as the honored author mine would be at the head of the table.

However, the woman was counting heads and realized there were 18 people for 16 seats. She came up to us and asked, "What are you doing here?"

"We're here for the 'Authors Night' dinner," then added with what I hoped was impressive fair, "I'm your guest author, Tom Clavin."

"You're not my guest author," she said, straining to be polite. "You're at the wrong party."

Dear readers, you might think this was embarrassing enough, but the true horror of our situation was about to be revealed. "That is something," I mused, trying to excuse my gaffe and save some face, "that there would be two author parties on the same street."

The hostess stared at me, and that is when I understood: This was not an author dinner at all but a gathering of friends, and it was being assumed that we had crashed a private party. And we had.

We high-tailed it back across the lush lawn. The two valets were nowhere to be found; they may have been smoking a joint in one of the real guests' cars. We managed to locate the keys, got in my car, and drove away. Only later did I wonder if the valets reported a car had been stolen.

We literally stopped a motorist on the street – the poor man probably thought he was being carjacked – to ask where the Jane Smith residence was. He told us it was next to Spielberg's house. "Have you been there before?' he asked.

I shook my head mournfully, acknowledging that I was not nearly famous enough for that.

About the Author
Tom Clavin

Tom Clavin is the author/co-author of 18 books, including the two more recent ones, *Lightning Down: A World War II Story of Survival* and, with Phil Keith, *To the Uttermost Ends of the Earth*. He lives, un-famously, in Sag Harbor.

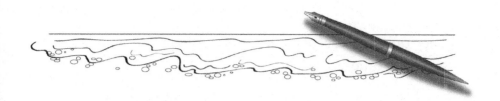

A TRIP TO JUNGLELAND - APRIL 28, 1979

by

Paul DiSclafani

As we approached our destination, the lizard-cabbie pulled up to the curb under the Madison Square Garden marquee, directly in front of the stairs and escalators leading from the street level into the bowels of Penn Station. We only had a few minutes to make that final 2:30 am Babylon train, so time was of the essence. The next train didn't depart for another three hours.

Unfortunately, my four friends were still entangled in a friendly full-scale wrestling match in the back of the oversized cab. As I opened the door, they spilled out onto the sidewalk laughing and giggling like a bunch of schoolgirls before regaining their composure.

The Big Man grabbed Douglas and said, "Come with me." He then turned to my brother and Mr. B, who were still sitting on the sidewalk. "We'll run down to the platform and hold the doors until you guys get there."

They quickly descended the deserted steps two and three steps at a time.

I stayed behind for a minute, rummaging through my pockets, hoping to find any paper money. Locating a crumpled paper bill, I carefully opened it hoping to see President Andrew Jackson's smiling face and not George Washington's. My scrambled brain was unsure what the rotating numbers for the fare finally stopped at, but ten bucks most likely included a good tip for a short trip to New York's Penn Station. I handed it to the lizard-cabbie and hoped for the best...

LET'S START AT THE BEGINNING

How did we get into this situation?

This trip started as just a couple of Long Island guys traveling by train from the suburbs into The Big City (Bruce Springsteen referred to it as "Jungleland") on a Saturday night in the Spring of 1979. We had nothing planned and no destination except catching the 9:05 pm Long Island Railroad train to Penn Station from Massapequa Park.

I was accompanied on this adventure by my friends Bruce (Mr. B), Greg (the Big Man), and Douglas (who for some reason never acquired a nickname), along with my younger brother Tony. Tony was given several nicknames over the years, but the one that stuck most often was a derivative of my nickname (Disco), with most calling him "Little Disco."

Pressed for time, our first stop was the liquor store for Peppermint Schnapps and Southern Comfort, then to Foodtown for beer. Unfortunately, they didn't stock cold beer.

"This is bullshit," Douglas said as he reached into the paper bag and took a swig of the already opened bottle of Southern Comfort, "I'm not drinking warm beer."

"I got an idea," Mr. B said, pointing to some cardboard boxes that were stashed nearby. "Look, instant coolers!"

With the clock ticking, we grabbed two boxes and a couple of bags of ice, and we were ready to go.

My brother Tony's blue, 2-door, 1965 Buick was nicknamed the "Beast of Burden." The "Beast" had served him (and us) well, but it was time to move on to bigger and better machines of destruction. This was the car's last trip as he had invested in a white 1965 van and was taking possession the next day.

We flew out of Foodtown, and while approaching the

Massapequa Park train station, we could see the 9:05 pulling in. Tony yelled out, "Time for Plan B!" and gunned it down Sunrise Highway. The only thing left to do was race the train until we got far enough in front of it.

We put enough distance between the train and us as we got to Wantagh. Although we beat the train to the station, the train had already pulled in when we parked and grabbed our essentials. As we raced up the stairs, we heard the recorded announcement, "Please stand clear of the closing doors." Luckily, the doors were still open when we got to the platform.

Gasping for breath and sweating like pigs despite the cool spring evening, we grabbed a set of facing seats. We toasted our timing and good fortune with our slightly chilled beers.

Even with all the scheduled stops, we would arrive at Penn Station in less than an hour. Since we wanted no part of dragging wet cardboard boxes of beer and melting ice through the streets of Manhattan, we needed to finish most, if not all, of what we had.

"So, what's the plan?" I asked innocently while taking a slug of Peppermint Schnapps when the bottle made its way into my hand.

"There ain't no plan," Mr. B said as I handed him the schnapps.

"I'm open for anything," The Big Man said, grabbing a fresh beer bottle and twisting the cap off with minimal spillage.

"What about Studio 54?" Little Disco said, piquing the interest of the entire group.

"You know we're not getting in, right?" I said.

"I didn't say we were getting in," Tony reiterated, "I just said we should go there. It's as good a destination as any, right?"

So, we toasted to Studio 54 and continued our attack on the colder beer until the train arrived at Penn Station.

With just a couple of beers remaining, Mr. B and the Big Man put them in their jacket pockets, and we exited the train. As I looked back to our seats to ensure we had everything, I felt terrible for the next passengers. Cardboard was never intended to hold melting ice and empty beer bottles.

Before heading to the surface, we stopped to take a quick supply inventory. Douglas reported half the schnapps was gone, while Tony noted we had plenty of Southern Comfort. Mr. B had one beer left in his jacket pocket while Big Man and I finished his beers.

We headed up to the surface at the Eighth Avenue end of the Garden, quickly stopping at the deli across the

271

street for a few cold six-packs of beer. Assuming Studio 54 was on 54th street, we headed uptown for the 20-block trek.

HIJINKS OUTSIDE OF STUDIO 54

A giant black marquee was over the entrance, displaying the iconic "54" in bright white. A long line of people dressed to the nines was waiting. Next door was a huge parking garage. Eyeballing the different types of people on the line, it was apparent five drunk guys wearing T-Shirts, jeans, and sneakers weren't getting in.

Planting ourselves on the sidewalk just outside the entrance to the parking garage, we settled in to finish off our current inventory of alcohol. We could use the bathroom inside the garage and comment on every loser that got rejected while they shuffled past us.

Some chick walked by us without a top on trying to get in but was rejected. How do you reject a topless chick with a great rack? Just then, two important-looking people exited a limo, along with the driver. They headed to the front of the line, leaving the limo with the motor running right in front of us.

"You think those guys are getting in?" I asked my

brother as he finished off the last of the Southern Comfort.

"Who cares," he said with a devilish grin. "They left the car running. I'm going to take it for a spin around the Block."

"I'm going with you," said Douglas as he tried to get up from a sitting position on the curb, only to think better of it.

Before I realized what was happening, Tony opened the driver's side door just as the actual driver returned bug-eyed and shouted obscenities. As he was being yanked away from the door, he did manage to grab a sharpie from the dashboard as a souvenir.

Soon, the two former occupants headed dejectedly back to the limo, losers, just like everyone else.

"Aw, fellas," said the Big Man sarcastically, "Couldn't get in?"

"Fuck you, assholes," one of them yelled back before getting inside the limo and slamming the door.

THE PENCIL-THIN JOINT

I needed to pee again, so I headed back to the bathroom. Inside were two guys smoking one of the thinnest joints I had ever seen, but they were totally wasted. While I headed to the urinal to do my business, they started a conversation with me just as my brother Tony came in.

Soon, the four of us were chatting like old friends. One of them whipped out another of those tiny joints to share during our conversation. We joined them, figuring we couldn't get more fucked up than we already were. We took two hits each when the Big Man came crashing in to do his business and joined us for a couple of hits.

We thanked the strangers for their hospitality and headed back to the street level. Unfortunately, Douglas and Mr. B were nowhere to be found. The two paper bags containing the empty beer cans were there, but they were not.

Tony noticed a neon sign across the street that simply said, "Bar."

Of course. Where else would they be?

Making our way quickly across the street, we opened the door and found both Douglas and Mr. B with bottles of Budweiser in their hands.

It was a classic "dive" bar, sitting directly across the street from one of the world's most famous nightclubs. It was packed with people, like us, that would never get into

Studio 54. In the corner was a small stage where a comedian was telling jokes. The crowd mostly ignored him, but we couldn't resist breaking his balls.

The Big Man and Mr. B were laughing way too loudly at his unfunny jokes, probably getting more laughs from the crowd than the comedian. He then launched a joke about a fire in an apartment building in Pittsburgh. Douglas recognized it immediately and whispered something to Mr. B.

"A young boy was being dangled by his mother outside of a window in the burning building when he slipped from her grip," the guy said. "Just then, the great receiver for the Pittsburgh Steelers, Lynn Swan, walked by. Swan reaches out and catches the boy before he hits the ground and saves his life!"

"Then he spikes him," Mr. B yelled out before the guy could deliver the punchline, stealing all the laughs from the crowd.

"Oh, you've heard that one before," the guy said as the rowdy crowd began booing him off the stage. Mr. B and Douglas just had huge smiles on their faces.

Making my way around to the other side of the bar, I found a pinball game in one of the back corners. However, when I tried to play it, I seemed to have lost control of my motor skills. Maybe there was a reason those guys in the bathroom were so wasted. What was in that tiny joint?

I stumbled back to the bar where The Big Man was and saw Tony, Mr. B, and Douglas exiting the bathroom with huge smiles. Citing "youthful exuberance," they punched a few holes in the bathroom wall as a going-away present. Not to be outdone, the Big Man and I entered the bathroom with the Devil's hands. By now, colors and bright lights were filling my head, and I thought I saw him tear off the toilet seat and stuff it inside his jacket for a souvenir. Since it was now close to 2 am, we had to get out of Dodge quickly to make the last train back to Wantagh.

We hailed a large capacity cab, so everyone piled into the back. Mr. B, Douglas, and the Big Man spread out over the back seat while Tony and I sat on the tiny side seats. Big Man handed me the toilet seat, which I promptly placed around my neck for safekeeping. I leaned over into the front seat and chatted with the cabbie about Hunter S. Thompson's "Fear and Loathing in Las Vegas." I suddenly felt I was channeling the gonzo journalist and thought I might be speaking to a lizard person.

Without warning, the other four maniacs in the back decided to start pushing each other. Soon, we had a full-scale rumble in the cab's backseat as it headed down 7th Avenue. The funny thing is, the lizard-cabbie never broke stride. Something told me he had weathered this type of storm before. When you drive a cab in The Big Apple, a little rumble in your back seat is not much to sneeze at.

BACK AT PENN STATION

Time was of the essence when we pulled up at the entrance to Penn Station. I managed to open the cab door, and the four wrestling maniacs spilled out onto the sidewalk. Two of them were already flying down the stairs to hold the train for us while I was fumbling in my pockets for money to pay the lizard-cabbie.

Approaching the entrance, Mr. B found a stray beer bottle in his jacket pocket and tossed it to my brother Tony, who was right behind him. This caught the attention of a police officer, who, after initially ignoring the fact that four inebriated individuals had just rolled out of the back seat of a yellow cab, yelled for them to stop. Instead, they raced down the stairs at a high rate of speed. I froze and watched as the scene unfolded below me from the street level.

Once at the bottom of the stairs, the Big Man appeared out of nowhere and blindsided Tony, causing him to go flying while the beer shattered on the tile floor.

With an officer heading down the steps yelling for them to stop, they scrambled in different directions to avoid being caught.

They were gone from sight as I chose the escalator to provide my long, slow descent into the bowels of Penn Station. Having witnessed the police chasing my friends, I tried my best not to be noticed. Someone would need to have a straightforward yet foggy head when it was time to bail them out of jail. The police were right behind them, and I could hear the static from their walkie-talkies.

Approaching the bottom of the escalator, two cops were staring at me. They couldn't possibly know I was with them, so I calmly walked past them, nodding my head and simply acknowledging them with a quick, "Officers, how are you tonight?" As I walked past triumphantly, one of them turned to me and said, "Hey you!"

"Yes?" I said, slowly turning to face them. "Where are you going?"

"Home, officer. Why do you ask?"

"Well, just wondering why you have a toilet seat around your neck?"

Busted.

They had me cold. I was drunk and walking around

Penn Station with a disgusting toilet seat around my neck.

"Oh, this old thing?" I said with a smile, removing the toilet seat from around my neck and slowly placing it on the floor.

Without saying another word, I turned and kept walking. I guess he was more concerned with the four maniacs running through Penn Station than some idiot with a toilet seat around his neck.

As I approached Track 17, someone called my name. Both Big Man and Douglas were hiding inside the LIRR bathroom corridor, peeking through the opening. I saw Tony hiding behind a pole and Mr. B calmly pretending to talk on a payphone while a cop walked right past him. They had pulled it off!

Once safely on the train, The Big Man was the first to pass out. With a sly smile on his face, Tony removed the sharpie from his pocket and stealthily approached the now snoring Big Man. He gently wrote, in big letters, "I'M GAY" on the fingers of his left hand and "HOMO" on the right. It was not unlike what the Lilliputians must have felt when approaching and subduing a sleeping Gulliver. Each letter Tony administered brought more and more anticipation of him waking up and killing each of us. Eventually, he would find out what happened, but the Lilliputians scored a massive victory for now!

ONE LAST RUMBLE IN THE BEAST

We arrived at Wantagh around 3:30 am and decided to stop at Jack-In-The-Box in Copiague for a late snack. Piling into the back seat of The Beast, we headed to Lindenhurst for tacos and burgers. Mr. B rode shotgun, and I was part of the back-seat trio with Big Man and Douglas. Douglas pointed out to Big Man that something was written on his hands.

Not a good idea.

Unfortunately for me, closest to Gulliver, I took the brunt of his vengeance before it turned into another full-scale rumble. Mr. B jumped over the seat to join the fray. Unlike the cabbie, Tony could not drive with a rumble in his backseat, so he pulled the car over to the shoulder and joined in.

While we were rumbling and destroying the interior of the Beast, which was history after tonight anyway, Douglas decided to add some spice to the equation and kicked the still-idling car into "Drive."

Now, we were rolling down the shoulder of Sunrise Highway at an idle speed with five maniacs rumbling in the backseat and the driver-side door wide open. When he realized we were moving, Tony jumped out of the car and ran stride for stride with the slow-moving vehicle, eventually grabbing the driver's door and jumping back into the seat. He calmly resumed the drive to Jack-in-the-Box while the rumble continued behind him.

I pity anyone who set eyes on us inside Jack-in-the-Box. We left with five maniacs and returned with five maniacs, which was all that mattered. I just felt sorry for the poor slob expecting to use the toilet seat inside that bar across from Studio 54.

Sitting at the table semi-conscience, I remember seeing the sun coming up through the window. Before I could say anything, the Big Man pointed out the window and said, "Uh, oh. Here comes tomorrow..."

About the Author
Paul DiSclafani

Paul DiSclafani, a Massapequa resident since 1967, is an award- winning columnist and published author. His weekly column "Long Island Living" appears locally throughout Nassau County. The Press Club of Long Island recognized "Long Island Living" with a "Best Column" award in 2021.

www.pauldisclafani.com

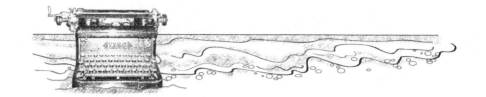

JUST WHY WAS DARWIN THERE?

by

Eric Forsyth

"I discovered the basic facts in the article when I was reading up on Patagonia, the Chilean Canals and the Beagle Channel in preparation for the cruise there in 1998-1999. I frequently told the story to friends who were usually amused. So I decided to write it down and I submitted it to "Ocean Navigator." They rejected it; too sexy I guess. In that case, I thought, it's just the thing for "Latitudes and Attitudes." They rejected it too, not sexy enough, I suppose. So rather than waste any more stamps I am going to post it on the FIONA web site."

Anyone who navigates in the wild channels on the southwest coast of Chile or ventures near the bleak rockbound shores south of Tierra Del Fuego into the Beagle Channel must be struck by the profusion of British names given to hundreds of bays, promontories and distinctive features. For example, entering the Canal

Cockburn near 550 S (the pilot warns to do so only in daylight in clear weather) you will find Cabo Gloucester, Bahia Euston, Bahia Laura and Bahia Otway. These names were given during surveys by the Royal Navy, which explored and charted the forbidding wastes starting about 1826. Ever suspicious of the French after the end of the Napoleonic wars in 1815, the Admiralty kept a large body of trained seamen on the books by engaging in a vast program of exploration of the world's more remote places. One of the ships dispatched literally to the end of the earth to chart the desolate and wind-swept coast north of Cape Horn was the Beagle, destined, of course, to achieve lasting fame when its famous supernumerary, Charles Darwin, postulated the Theory of Evolution many years later. Incidentally, he also gave rise to Darwin Cordillera, Isla, Monte, Narrows and Paso on the charts. The seeds of the theory were first sown in Darwin's mind by observations he made during his five-year cruise aboard the Beagle. But how Darwin came to be on the Beagle in the first place is a tantalizing mystery, and at least one explanation implies the world of science owes Darwin's Theory to a rather unpleasant member of the local Yaghan Indian tribe nicknamed York Minster.

Four Indians wound up aboard the Beagle during its first cruise, 1826 to 1830. The skipper, Captain Stokes, had committed suicide and Captain Fitzroy was appointed

286

in his place to complete the tour. Stokes is remembered by two Bahias, two Cabos, Monte, Ensenada, Punta and Surgidero (anchorage). Towards the end of the cruise Yaghan Indians stole the whaleboat which was vital for surveying the smaller bays and creeks inaccessible to the Beagle. Fitzroy made furious attempts to get it back, finally kidnapping the four Indians as bargaining chips. Unfortunately for Fitzroy, the Yaghans were a very primitive society with no chiefs and no concept of property. So there was really no one to bargain with and he never got the whaleboat back. At this stage he decided to take the natives back to England, his justification being that they could return in a few years speaking English, and trained in rudimentary agriculture so that the tribe could begin to lead a better life. Most important of all, for Fitzroy was deeply religious, they could become Christians. He argued the action could also help any sailors who might be shipwrecked on the coast in future years. The admiral commanding the South American station gave Fitzroy permission to transport them on a navy ship to England, all subsequent expenses to be borne by Fitzroy himself. It should be mentioned that Fitzroy was independently wealthy and came from a politically well-connected family, which traced its descent from an illegitimate child of Barbara Villiers, the powerful mistress of King Charles II.

On arrival in England in late 1830 one of the Indians contracted smallpox and died. The remaining three were packed off to a quiet village to receive an education in English and Christian values from two Church of England clergymen. Also keeping an eye on them was the coxswain of the Beagle, James Bennett, who doubtless kept Fitzroy briefed. News of the strange denizens of an unimaginably remote part of the world titillated London society and ultimately, in 1831, Fitzroy was commanded to bring them to an audience with King William and Queen Adelaide. The youngest of the Indians was a girl the sailors called Fuegia Basket, because she had originally been hauled up the side of the ship in a wicker basket. At that time she was about ten years old. Next to her in age was a young boy called Jemmy Button, so called because Fitzroy gave his father a mother-of -pearl button for him. Both Fuegia Basket and Jemmy were bright children who rapidly picked up a smattering of English and adapted quickly to the life into which they had been thrust. York Minster, by contrast, was probably in his twenties and was slow to learn, truculent and generally unhappy. Queen Adelaide was very taken by Fuegia Basket; she gave her a bonnet, a ring and some money. All the officers that were even remotely connected with the Beagle's voyage were suitably honored by the royal attention.

After the audience things went downhill and the mystery begins: in the summer of 1831, less than a year after the Beagle's arrival, Fitzroy suddenly decided to take the Indians back to Patagonia, but why so quickly? As the Admiralty was not planning to send the Beagle back to South America for at least two years, Fitzroy applied for a year's leave of absence and hired a privately owned schooner to take the party back. This set him back about a thousand pounds, a substantial sum in those days. Riesenberg in his history of Cape Horn suggests that James Bennett caught Fuegia Basket and York Minster in flagrante delicto and communicated this to Captain Fitzroy. Just the news that the hulking York Minster was enjoying the favors of an underage girl would have been disastrous for Fitzroy's career considering the royal interest. Worse, suppose she became pregnant? No wonder Fitzroy put together an expedition at lightning speed. This reason for Fitzroy's haste is not supported by other historians, although it is extremely unlikely that anything was written about the matter and the speed with which Fitzroy moved is circumstantial supporting evidence. At this stage perhaps the reason for Fitzroy's trip was whispered in the highest echelons of the government. A well-placed relative, Lord Londonderry, leaned on the Admiralty and suddenly the Beagle was ordered back to South America. In fact, Fitzroy forfeited the money he had already paid for the schooner charter. Of course, some kind of cover story was needed for this change of heart – enter Darwin. He would be charged to study the strange fora and fauna in remote Patagonia and points west. Ironically, both Fitzroy and Darwin believed the studies would confirm the story of creation told in Genesis. Fitzroy moved the Indians to Plymouth in October 1831, where they were directly under his eye and out of the London spotlight. Repairs and modifications to the Beagle were rapidly completed and after a couple of false starts caused by bad weather the expedition left England just after Christmas, 1831. Besides Darwin there was a missionary who planned to disembark with the Indians when they got back to the Beagle channel. What happened to Darwin is history. What happened to the Indians, the missionary, and the subsequent attempts to civilize the region is also a fascinating history, but that is another story.

FURTHER READING:

Felix Riesenberg. Cape Horn, Dodd, Mead and Co, New York, 1939.

H. E. L. Mellersh. Fitzroy of the Beagle, Rupert Hart-Davis, London, 1968.

Alan Morehead. Darwin and the Beagle, Hamish Hamilton, London, 1969.

R. E. Marks. Three Men of the Beagle, Alfred A. Knopf, New York, 1991.

About the Author
Eric Forsyth

Eric Forsyth was born in England, attended Manchester University, served as an RAF fighter pilot and immigrated to Canada. After gaining a commercial pilot license he enrolled in the University of Toronto Engineering Graduate School and worked at Brookhaven National Laboratory. He retired and spends his time ocean sailing.

293

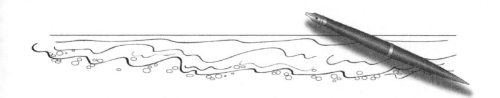

PAIN VIN FROMAGE

by

Elaine Gilmartin

Pain, vin, et fromage! became our rallying cry, but our journey was not a seamless one. Separated by geography with one daughter on the west coast, the other in London, amidst a pandemic, my daughters and I wanted to meet up somewhere new and exciting, Paris readily coming to mind. The announcement France would open to international travelers on June 9, 2021, was all we needed to hear!

My older daughter, Sarah, was tasked with the itinerary and was the one who discovered Pain Vin Fromage, a fondue restaurant on a quiet Paris side street. What could be better than warm bread, a good bottle of red wine-or two-and melty cheese? Nothing I know.

Sarah and I met at Heathrow Airport, separate flights conveniently landing half an hour apart. A quick hug followed by an Uber ride into the heart of London brought us to the flat of my younger daughter, Kate, on Pocock Street, where she awaited us with COVID tests.

Yes, to fly into the UK we needed proof of negative antigen tests and similarly, France would require the same prior to entry on the 9th. Once completed, we sealed the test kits and put them in a Dropbox to be forgotten until the expected e-mail response within a day or so.

And off we went, jet lag be damned! A delish avocado toast brunch fueled us for a tour at the Tower of London and a foray to The Clink, a thousand-year-old dungeon prone to flooding due to its proximity to the Thames. After these history lessons on the limits of human suffering, we enjoyed a few pints at Covent Gardens, savoring the beauty of the late spring day while listening to street entertainers.

If it were not for the ubiquitous masks on passersby, one could forget we remained mired in a pandemic. So much so, that the following day as we toured the city of Oxford, Sarah asked Kate how we would be notified of our test results on which our entry to France rested.

Scrolling through her phone, Kate's expression went from benign indifference to blatant panic. Watching this evolution unfold, Sarah's expression became one of consternation, demanding to know if we were all positive.

Thankfully no, but Kate's eyes belied bad news as she

confessed she had forgotten to include the necessary bar codes for scanning test results to the recipient.

Reality hit us all instantly. As travel was still mostly novel at this point in the pandemic, tests were expensive and not easy to come by, each costing about a hundred pounds. And we would need the results for our Paris train ride Wednesday morning.

Sarah admitted to me later she wanted to throttle her little sister but restrained the impulse. We all needed to be calm and clear-headed and, as we had a much-needed drink at the Varsity Club in Oxford, we mobilized our brainpower. If we did not get tests ASAP, *Pain Vin Fromage* would be nothing more than a dream.

Okay, we found two appointments for that night, but they could not possibly accommodate a third. Ugh. Persistence prevailed and we found one appointment at another location and grabbed it, necessitating a harried, sweaty run through the streets of London.

Tested for the second time that day, we were thoroughly exhausted and a late dinner at the Moon Under Water in Leicester Square renewed our spirits if not our strength.

The morning of June 9th we rose early, and we rose with trepidation. An early train at 8 AM, *excusez-moi, a huit heures*, meant those results better be in! Rolling our suitcases along the London streets, each of us continually refreshing e-mail on our respective phones, my older daughter doing so while balancing a coffee cup in hand, my nerves were shot. Despite that, I kept smiling and offering empty reassurances as any good mom would do.

If the results did not come through, I thought possibly I could bluster my way through the immigration check, pretending to be the ignorant and hopeless American who just had to get her daughters to see Paris. Would they show mercy?

Entering the station and viewing the French border police at the gate dashed that idea immediately and rightly so. They were trying to contain a worldwide pandemic; we merely sought melty cheese.

"I'm negative!" Kate suddenly declared.

Within moments, my results came through, corroborating my belief it would be negative. I looked to my older daughter, scrolling through her phone, her anxiety palpable. She tossed out her empty coffee cup, her frustration evident.

Sarah is a planner. She works hard as an attorney, working long hours, work seeps into her weekends, weeks blurring into the next as vacations are a rarity. And with the pandemic straining everyone's emotional well-being, families separated, grappling with illness, this would be a much-needed reprieve and I wanted it for her more than myself.

So, standing there eyeing the French border police, the only barrier to passing through customs enroute to the waiting train, I momentarily imagined creating a distraction and racing my daughters through, but cooler heads needn't prevail as she received her text alert. She was indeed negative.

"Allons-y!" I cried in triumph, my high school French briefly surfacing in my stressed brain. As we proudly showed our negative COVID status and passports, we ran to the waiting train, with only twenty minutes to spare.

Giddy with relief as we crossed under the English Channel, we reviewed our itinerary for the next four days with great anticipation. We would begin with Sacre-Coeur Basilica, dinner at a restaurant in Montmarte, a tour of the Louvre and Musee D'Orsay. A descent into the French Catacombs, strolling and shopping along the Champs-Elysees and visiting l'Arc de Triomphe. A full day at the Palace of Versailles, and then our final night in Paris to be celebrated at Pain Vin Fromage. We accepted with some resignation that we could not enter the damaged Notre Dame, nor could we ascend to the top of the Eiffel Tower due to renovations, but we would still be able to stand in the presence of history in all its beauty.

Among the first of the international travelers, we were stunned by the outpouring of hospitality we were shown at each and every destination, every cafe and restaurant, as each Parisian voiced some variation of the hardship throughout the pandemic.

Dependent on tourism, shopping, entertainment, first-rate restaurants, Paris was hit quite hard by the circumstances of the pandemic. Much unlike many American households, Parisians live in relatively small apartments with many of its residents employed in fields directly impacted by the shutdown. Working a remote position in the comfort of my two-floor home and expansive backyard for the past year and some months, I experienced empathy and guilt in equal measure, and yet, our hosts across the ocean could not have been more kind, more welcoming, and more pleased to embrace a lifelong since on hold.

My daughters and I in turn embraced this return to living. We walked miles, circling the damaged Notre Dame still in awe of its beauty. We ate croissants and Croque- Monsieurs and we drank good wine. We engaged with shop proprietors, my fledgling efforts to converse in a language I hadn't used since high school met with kind patience and encouragement. We stood in the presence of the Mona Lisa with no crowds to battle, we were able to savor the works of Monet and Gaughin and Van Gogh.

We descended into the Catacombs of Paris, the three of us walking in lockstep through the subterranean tunnels with nary another tourist in sight, the skulls and bones of six million people bearing silent witness.

Then there was the sheer delight of the Palace of Versailles, its decadence in equal measure stunning in its opulence, off-putting in its ostentatious display of wealth. Walking the grounds provided spontaneous shows of water fountains synchronized with music, culminating in the night sky alive with fireworks.

Once back in the heart of Paris, we had energy to spare. A curfew remained in place with police sweeping the streets at 11 PM to usher everyone home, but with recently loosened restrictions, the streets remained just as crowded at 10:59 PM. The three of us walked down to the Seine, a bottle of wine to share, to watch the lights of the Eiffel Tower.

Seated on a low brick wall, we savored the beautiful night, the Paris skyline glittering in stark contrast to the darkness. Occasional passersby would strike up conversations, forcing me to recall those long-dormant lessons given that both my daughters studied Spanish in high school. It did not escape me that most of these interactions involved young men trying to engage with my daughters. Two rather persistent ones began using their

301

phones for translation, likely not impressed with my efforts to convey their questions, much to my relief.

With the 11 PM curfew rapidly approaching, I walked a bit to throw out our empty wine bottle and cups and was surprised when I returned moments later to see my older daughter seated alone scrolling through her phone. Glancing up at me, she calmly informed me Kate had walked off a bit with the guys to meet up with their friend who was fluent in both French and English.

Heart sinking, I peppered her with questions *Whaddaya mean she went off with them? Which direction did they go? What was she thinking?*

Not an alarmist by nature, I began to feel growing panic as my eyes scanned the crowds at the bank of the Seine, people happily milling about, laughing, talking excitedly, the French police still a distance away as they prepared to sweep the area for curfew. With minimal light from the glowing Eiffel Tower reflecting off the Seine, it would not be easy to find her as my fears she was already abducted began to fill my head.

I was prepared to go full Liam Neeson a la *Taken*, when suddenly she appeared at my side, pleased to show me pictures they took, contacts shared once they had a qualified translator. So the two young men turned out to be harmless students now Instagram followers of my daughter, not some nefarious members of a criminal enterprise. The relief I felt was palpable and right on cue, as the police began their evening ritual to clear the streets for curfew.

My momentary panic became fodder for my daughters' teasing as the three of us sat outdoors on a quiet Paris side street, a basket of bread, a bottle of wine, and a huge bubbly pot of melty cheese on the table in front of us. And as the kind wait staff tended to us on our final night in their beautiful city, it did not escape me the preciousness of this moment. That it would take a journey across an ocean to a magical destination to remind me of what I hold most dear, that sometimes we are called to step out of the mundane, the routine, to embrace what is closest to our hearts. And on my solo fight back to New York, I carried with me the joy that was *Pain, Vin, et Fromage*!

About the Author
Elaine Gilmartin

I am a therapist by profession, which is a great career for writers because I get into people's heads and hear stories that can seem too fantastic even for fiction. It's also helpful in that it is my job to challenge how they perceive themselves and the world around them, not always an easy task! I write articles for the online site Medium and love to start each day with a long run.

UP, DOWN AND UP

by

Paula Groothuis

Life can start in many ways and can be experienced with different emotions taking us up and down, down and up. A little girl, named Dolly, was born many years ago into a wonderful loving supportive family, which included her parents and big brothers along with grandparents, aunts, uncles, and cousins. Her memories from childhood are rare but she remembers when she rode a bike to her friend's house and went inside. When she came out, the bicycle was gone. A brother had moved it to teach her to be more careful, so things stay safe. Each brother loved to teach her as well as tease her and make her laugh. To this day, they are there for her. Dolly was certainly a lucky child.

Dolly went to a nursery school and then off to kindergarten which brings back one memory. The teacher was very strict, and Dolly did not like the way she was spoken to, and there was some project that wasn't working for her. She remembers standing at the bottom of the steps at home, looking up at her beautiful mother and telling Mom that she did not want to go back to school. They talked about it and Mom spoke to the principal and Dolly was moved to a different class which Dolly recalls worked out well. School continued and she'll never forget Dad being invited to school to talk to the principal regarding little Dolly's abilities in school. She was so bright that, in the middle of 2nd grade, she was moved to 3rd grade. Things are looking UP for Dolly.

There are other smaller memories of fun time on the block particularly when the ice cream truck came down throughout the summer and she would run up and down the block with friends. She recalls a conversation with Dad about taking a bus into the shopping area which was something her friend was not allowed to do, but Dad treated her with such respect even as a little girl. After the conversation, he said yes, and Dolly was lucky again.

Her wonderful Mom, who was a professional singer wasn't very healthy at a certain point. Dolly remembers so many songs that Mom would sing from Carousel, Most Happy Fella, Damn Yankees, Oklahoma, and many more. But Mom passed away when Dolly was turning eight years old. Her grandpa said Mom was now an angel up in heaven. Was Dolly too young to comprehend the loss?

308

Children sometimes cannot process feeling surrounding the loss of a parent. Will she address this later?

While she was not happy about it, she was treated with so much love and support as a little girl, she didn't feel the pain that one would expect. She doesn't remember grieving. All her needs were met. She felt loved and she was always a good little girl, polite, kind, and obedient. Basically, Dolly was a good girl, except for lying. A little. She had learned that white lies were sometimes necessary not to hurt peoples' feelings, but she did lie occasionally when she wanted to do something her parents said no to, that she really wanted. But again, all was going well.

Not too long after, Dad introduced Dolly to a woman who became her stepmom. They moved to another house in another area. Little Dolly moved on. Her new mom had her own boys too, and now was able to take a little girl shopping for adorable girl clothes. The new school wanted to put her into 4th grade due to her age, but her stepmom stood up for her bright stepdaughter and Dolly was moved into 5th grade since she had skipped a grade. School went well for years, and Dolly became a leader in high school. She also went off to summer camp for many years and loved it and became a leader there as well. Dolly's life is full of UPs again, thanks to her lucky break with a wonderful stepmother.

Then she was off to college with no idea what she wanted to study. Her favorite subject was math, but she didn't want to be a teacher. She thought about going into business, but Dad told her it wasn't a field for a woman, which was true back then, and she almost always listened to her dad. She visited her boyfriend from high school but never told her parents because it was something they didn't want her to do. They didn't want her to travel so far on her own. She liked him a lot, but he had a temper which bothered her. Then she met someone in college who made her feel calm, appreciated, and secure. She started dating him and, right after college, they got married. She got pregnant but unluckily had a miscarriage and needed surgery. She prayed that she would be back to the hospital the following year for a happier reason. She had started a job before she was pregnant and worked for a few years. She didn't love it, but, as soon as she got pregnant again, she left the field. One year after surgery her prayer came true, and she gave birth; the happiest day of her life.

She loved holding that baby in her arms and wanted her to be a happy, confident, good soul in the world. As a parent to a toddler, once in a while, Dolly, as a mother, was somewhat angry at her little girl. Why does a mother yell at a little girl who she loves more than anyone in the world? Dolly read books and attended workshops in which various 'tools' were used throughout the years; granting in fantasy what one can't have in reality, giving choices, accepting feelings and more. Dolly recalls using these tools to handle situations with both her children, something Dolly is so thankful for to this day. Dolly is on the UP swing again.

One day her daughter brought home a flyer about community theater. Dolly had been in shows in school and at camp and loved to sing and act. She must have gotten these traits from her long-ago-in-memory mother. She got the lead in the show which had a romantic part to it. At the dress rehearsal a real kiss took place. Apparently, Dolly had never experienced chemistry.

She had married a man who made her feel secure, but again, she had never experienced such chemistry. Life moved on to an affair, a divorce, a new marriage. Was this the right man? A few years later, another divorce took place. There were quite a few years in which Dolly could not stop crying. Was she feeling guilty about being divorced twice? How did this affect her kids? Was she actually finally grieving the loss of her mother? She never meant to hurt anyone, and she never meant to do anything wrong.

Who was this good little girl now? She was single and dated different men for a few years. One was a nice guy

311

with ADHD.

Dolly had enjoyed rhyming as a teenager. She found thank you notes repetitious and boring and had fun turning them into rhyme. Then as a divorced woman, she rhymed a lot of thoughts to release her emotions. The ADHD temporary boyfriend had written a book and asked Dolly to take a class to learn about publishing. Due to that experience, Dolly ended up self-publishing a large group of her emotional rhymes. She invited friends and family over for a book signing. A few weeks later, she got a call from her cousin who usually came for any family event. He had not received the invitation because he and his wife had separated. He no longer lived in his house, so he didn't get his mail on time. Dolly did not know that, and then she got together with her sweet loving cousin. They fell in love and finally, the love, support and chemistry were there for her.

Dolly was finally in the right relationship. She had gone back to work, enjoyed parenting and loved working with children and helping them to learn and grow. There were no more tears coming down her face. These days, she is in a happy relationship, enjoys her family and friends, loves her work, keeps singing and acting, keeps busy with sports and exercise. She began rhyming children's books to teach different messages. Dolly could not be prouder of the children she raised, who they are today and how they raise their children. Dolly finds it interesting how the negative memories from the past can actually have some value. If she had not needed to go back to work, she would never have gone back to help children which she is enjoying today. She has truly learned from her mistakes, to let go of the past and value the appreciation of all that she has today. She was able to turn her mistakes into steppingstones toward a more generous and peaceful life. She has created inner peace. Dolly has truly moved on!

About the Author
Paula Groothuis

Paula is a speech therapist and an author living on Long Island. She is a mother of two grown children who she could not be prouder of. And now she is a proud grandmother as well. Through the years she found that writing was a way to express herself and get feelings and thoughts out. She has come out with two adult books and many children's books to teach all types of messages. She also had a business in which she would write poems for birthdays, anniversaries, retirements, and any other special occasion to honor people's families and friends. Writing keeps her busy and she never has nothing to do!

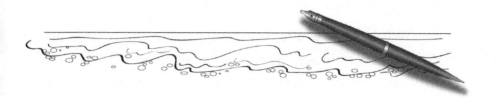

BEST BURGER EVER

by

Dr. John H.Krahn

I think it was the best burger I have ever eaten. A half- pound of charcoal-broiled Black Angus beef cooked to medium perfection . . . melted cheese on top, bacon, fried onions, and a special tangy sauce all housed in a toasted sesame seed bun. It was 1250 calories of deliciousness. And there were great French fries on the side for another 400 calories. The only fault I found with this meal was the posting of the calories on the menu. This has a way of dampening the enjoyment.

So when my wife and I were looking to eat out a month later, I welcomed the opportunity to frequent the same restaurant for a second helping of this fabulous bovine treat. It wasn't to be. The burger was served well done, really well done, even after I clearly ordered it to be medium.

When the waitress returned with the customary, "How's everything?" question, I showed her how the chef had charred my fabulous burger. When she offered to get me another, I demurred, for we had already waited a long time for the first order. A few minutes later, the manager graced our table with his apologies and insisted he brings me another burger cooked correctly. I reluctantly agreed. I had already made my way through half of my meal and was no longer hungry.

When we had finished, we paid the check and got ready to leave. The manager appeared yet again and said, "It will be ready in just a minute more, and I will wrap it up to go for you." He then presented me with a whole meal, a burger with all the fix-ins and French fries in a plastic box ready to travel. I thanked him and we left the restaurant. Exiting the restaurant parking lot, my wife and I discussed when we might be able to eat the extra meal, for we had a dinner engagement the following night.

As I was getting ready to turn into the main road, I spotted him. An apparently homeless man pushing a shopping cart with all of his possessions stuffed in it was walking up the road passing the restaurant where we just ate.

"I bet he might enjoy our extra meal," I said to my wife. I turned and parked on the side of the road. As he approached our car, I jumped out and said to him, "Sir, are you hungry?"

"Yes, I am," he answered me. The man was thin, in his fifties. His top four front teeth were missing. His clothes were basic and dirty. I quickly told him the story of my meal and that the restaurant manager had provided me another meal to take home. I told him that it was untouched, and I asked him whether or not he would like it. "Sure," he answered me with a big toothless grin.

Returning to my car, I grabbed the hot meal and handed it to him. "God bless you," he said to me.

"Eat it while it is hot," I encouraged him. As we drove away, I wondered whether he had been questioning where he might get his next meal. I bet he was both surprised and happy it came from a nice restaurant. I hoped he liked his hamburger cooked medium.

I was just grateful that I had the opportunity to share the best burger ever with a fellow human being.

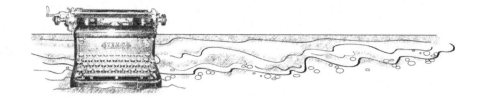

LIFE - MORE THAN A HYPHEN

by

Dr. John H.Krahn

The one consistent thing that you will find in every cemetery is the hyphen. Actually, you will see it on every gravestone. "John Doe 1943 - 2022." There it is, that little mark summing up John's 78 years of life. Kind of sad in a way. For some people, their lives are not remarkable at all. Their date of birth is connected to their date of death by that little, nearly nothing, mark we call the hyphen. It almost appears that nothing much worthwhile happened in John Doe's life. It is up to all of us individually to make sure our hyphens will represent a life that is fully lived, productive, meaningful, and joyful . . . that our lives are more than just a hyphen.

When I lived in Levittown, New York, our house had a very small bedroom on the first floor. It served as both the laundry room and my office. On the clothes dryer next to my desk was our family pet, a little gerbil. He inhabited

321

a large, rectangular, fish tank. A water dish and an exercise wheel were his furniture in the tank.

As I worked at my desk, often my gerbil friend would hop on his wheel and run as fast as he could. He would then stop, jump off, look around, and then get back on and run a little faster. Watching him, I wondered what he was thinking. Might it be, "If I can only run a little bit faster, I might get out of this crummy fish tank?"

I thought that this might be a parody of life. Sometimes this happens when we allow one nondescript day to flow into another, then into another. C.S. Lewis once wrote, "Where is the life we have lost in the living?" Life is a precious gift that we should decide to live to the fullest every day.

I once attended a funeral of a man who died about two months after he retired. Prior to his retirement, he worked as much overtime as he could in order to jack up his retirement pay. He even worked a second job to save even more money so he and his wife could travel and finally live the good life. Then he died before he could realize his dream. Tell me about a very sad funeral. No one holds a claim on tomorrow. We only have today to live to the fullest.

A college professor put several objects on a table before his students entered his classroom. After they were seated and quieted down, without saying anything, he took a very large, empty mayonnaise jar and set it in the middle of the table where every student could view it. He then filled the jar with golf balls. When the jar was filled to the top, he asked his class "Is the jar full?" They all nodded their heads that it was.

Next, the professor took a container with very small pebbles and carefully shook them into the jar filling the spaces around the golf balls. Once again, he queried his students, "Is the jar now full?" Smiling, they all said, "Yes." Again the professor took a third container filled with sand and carefully sifted it into the jar. Once again, he asked his students whether the jar was finally full. With one voice, they answered, "Yes," for they were now sure that nothing else would ft into the jar.

Finally, the professor produced two glasses of red wine and poured them into the mayonnaise jar. The students laughed. When the laughter subsided, the professor said, "Now I want you to think of the jar as representing your life. The golf balls are the important things: your health, your family, your faith, things that if every other thing was lost, your life would still be full."

"The pebbles are the other things that matter like your job, your house, and your car. And the sand is the small stuff. Now if you put the pebbles and the sand in the jar first, there would be no room for the golf balls. The same goes for your life. If you spend all of your time and energy fretting about and doing the small stuff, you will have no room left for the stuff that is most important to you. Pay attention to those things that are critical to your well-being and happiness. Take time and enjoy your family, eat healthily, and worship regularly. Always do the most important things first to have a great life."

One of his students raised her hand and inquired, "What about the wine; what did the two glasses of wine represent?" The professor smiled, "I'm glad you asked. It just proves that no matter how full your life may seem, there is always room for a glass of wine with a friend."

My life has been full. I have lived 78 years, more than my share. I have been relatively healthy, survived open-heart surgery and Covid. I am happily married with two fine children and three grandchildren. I have traveled extensively, had a long professional career, have written books, hold a doctor's degree, and am financially well off. And over the years, I have enjoyed many glasses of wine with friends.

One could argue that it is time for me to retire to an easy chair. But I do not want to waste the last chapter of my life. I'm thinking that it just might be the very best chapter of all. And my best chapter is highly unlikely to be lived in an easy chair. I want my gravestone hyphen to reflect a life lived to the fullest extent possible even to my last breath.

About the Author
Dr. John H. Krahn

Dr. John H. Krahn has authored 15 books. He is a much sought-after speaker and has led numerous workshops both nationally and internationally. Currently, he is the President of the Long Island Authors Group. Creating this LIAG Anthology was his idea.

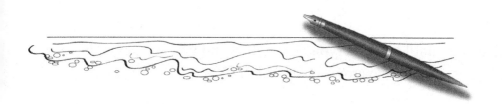

SOUTH SHORE GIRL IN A NORTH SHORE WORLD

by

Alice Reiter Laby

I was looking forward to Sunday, June 2, 2019, the day the town of Port Washington, on Long Island's North Shore, hosted a book and craft fair called Harborfest. Last year, on June 3, our home-grown writers from Long Island Authors Group had a successful day. Our books sold well, and Newsday interviewed several of us, yours truly included, and published an article the following week.

I was pleased Newsday told my story. I'm a senior citizen from Long Island's South Shore. I've written a romance novel set in Amsterdam entitled GOING DUTCH. I was delighted - several people at Harborfest 2018 told me they were happy they could buy real books on a pleasant Sunday.

Sad to say, Harborfest 2019 did not live up to 2018's success. Perhaps it was the weather forecast predicting thunderstorms in the afternoon, which didn't materialize until after everyone packed up and left. Whatever the cause, the crowds were thinner.

To soothe my disappointment, I queued up on the Ralph's Ices line, anticipating my chocolate delight. While waiting, I got talking to a young couple who just moved to Port Washington from Manhattan. When I mentioned I was a romance novelist and was selling my book at the Fest, the woman of the duo was interested. They followed me back to our booth.

I sat down at my table, adorned with a red cloth and several copies of GOING DUTCH, which has a suggestive cover photo of a woman holding a red tulip. My female guest picked up a copy of my book (yes), stared at the cover (yes yes), read the synopsis on the back (yes yes yes), and put the book back on the table.

"Too much sex," she said. "Not for me."

I was astounded! Too much sex?!

The day ended well though. I had made connections with three women who I thought could help provide a wider audience for GOING DUTCH.

I emailed those people. I have received a response from one woman, but not from the other two.

Was it my South Shore Strong Island personality that put them off? I'm definitely not a North Shore gal, not monied, not slim and fashionably dressed, but smart, friendly, loving, intelligent and welcoming diversity in my life.

I realized I had a lot to be thankful for. My three sons and their families are amazing. I have a good life with my boyfriend Rob; we live together in a condo development. Our neighbors are friendly - people say hello when I walk my senior citizen dog, which is often.

Recently, a handsome African American neighbor with two little dogs of his own asked, "Are you alright? Is your old pooch okay? I haven't seen you walking this week!"

I'm fIne, I reassured him, just busy traveling east on Sunrise Highway, helping with the grandkids. I am more than just fine - I am eternally grateful.

About the Author
Alice Reiter Laby

Alice was born and bred on Long Island, venturing off the Island to attend graduate school at Fordham University. She is the author of a romantic novel set in Amsterdam entitled *GOING DUTCH*, and is completing a World War 2 novel, and a memoir about her family's Eastern European roots.

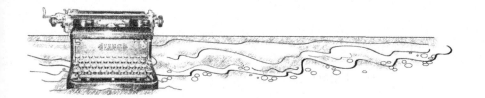

WHY ARE YOU STILL SINGLE?

by

Christine Maier

I was enjoying my five-day stay in an old farmhouse in Scotland at a writing retreat. The main room had a long wood table with a bench on each side; it served as both classroom and dining room. The chandelier illuminated the table for dinner with candles. On the other side of the main room was a fireplace with dark red couches and a mahogany coffee table nestled around it.

I took a bite into my haddock dinner as the creepy guy in the red and blue plaid shirt asked, "Why are you still single?" It wasn't a private, curious question. It was loud and accusatory. He had been bothering everyone during the week; he finally got to me.

It was the tone of the question that bothered me. I was immediately defensive and looked anywhere but at him. The eleven silent faces split their looks between their plates, me, and the fifty-something man who clearly had no manners.

"Well," I started to answer.

Before I could finish, the slim-toned woman in her forties interrupted, "You don't need to answer that." Emma wrote stories about her trainer but barely mentioned her husband. Despite her questionable marital status, I was happy for the help. I wasn't going to get much from the rest of the group as they were all happily married.

Except for Maggie, who was from Scotland. Where she lived, girls got married just out of high school. She was nineteen, single, and actively looking for a mate. She stared into her plate, shifting the haddock around. This moment was the opposite of her short stories about love and romance. I think my spinster status scared her, almost like she thought it was contagious. Or maybe she was just freaked out about my story where the husband was trying to hide a dead prostitute in the basement.

If I were to answer the creepy guy honestly, sometimes I worried I would be single forever, too, which is why plaid shirt's accusation pissed me off. I was forty-one with an established career, a co-op, and a sense of adventure. Yet, I had no one to come home to at night, no one to share a restaurant coupon with, no built-in partner, and no one to support the pursuit of my passions like Janet did.

From the seat next to me, Janet grabbed a roll to avoid looking at anyone. She had three kids out of the house and was trying to find herself. Her husband willingly went with her to all sorts of activities, but he drew the line at attending her writing workshops. Instead, he bought her the week-long writing retreat to help with her coming-of-age short stories. If I could find a guy who emotionally supported my passions like that, I wouldn't be single. I had dated on and off over the years, but balancing a career, travel, and the occasional uninspiring date, was challenging. Maybe I expected too much.

The only guy in my life was the upstairs neighbor, Thumper, aptly named after the non-romantic sounds coming from his apartment. He went into rages, throwing things, yelling, and cursing. We barely spoke, but I felt like I was in an abusive relationship when he yelled, "you prick," and threw a bowling ball. My complaints to building management only helped for a few days.

A loud upstairs neighbor is its own issue for apartment dwellers, but my relationship with Thumper extended outside my apartment. Several years ago, after the first rage incident, I ran into him at a white-water rafting dating event.

Outwardly, he seemed like a nice guy, friendly smile, manners, supported himself. He tried to talk to me, but I couldn't get the sounds of his rage out of my head. I asked the organizer to separate us. I couldn't take the risk that the one incident was the real him. It wasn't long before there were more incidents, confirming I made the right decision. They reminded me that being single can be scary.

I shifted in my seat. The question was still out there, and it needed an answer. Even if everyone else just wanted to move on.

I mustered bravado and said part of the truth, "I never met anyone I wanted to marry."

"Here." Sara, the young newlywed, offered me a glass of pity wine. She was still in the honeymoon stage. She must have felt bad that I didn't have someone to hang out with, travel with, and share my deepest darkest secrets with. While I wanted some wine, I didn't need the pity.

I wanted to stand up and say the truth. I didn't understand why we haven't moved past the days of thinking an unmarried woman would become the crazy cat lady, watching the world from her windows with a dozen cats? Did they fear for us, all alone with no one to protect us from the Thumpers of the world? Or were they afraid we would try to take over the world?

In the ten years I had lived alone, I never considered getting a cat. Yes, there was the occasional really bad day when even coming home to a cat might have made me feel better. Those were also the days when I learned the value of my family and friends. I could and did call on those days. In exchange, I retained a lot of freedom.

After dinner, the group split between cleaning up and preparing for our evening reading. James found me in the living room. "Don't worry about him," he said. But I couldn't help thinking that he had asked me why I was still single in roundabout ways during the week. He had a better delivery than plaid shirt. His path to the writing retreat couldn't have been more different than mine. He was in his fifties with no kids and had to get permission from his wife to attend. The retreat was only twenty minutes from where he lived. I know couples need to check with their partner before going away for a week without them. And I know for some couples it's an automatic no. Suddenly faced with this question, it struck me that the only one with veto power was my calendar, and it was more likely to encourage me to extend my trip. My calendar understood single.

"Thank you, James," I said.

As I climbed into bed that night, I felt content in my freedom; and it occurred to me that some of the things we think we need a partner for are societal myths. When I was a rookie cop and worked every Friday and Saturday night, it was hard to find someone to go to dinner or a movie with; I didn't bother asking to do both on a weeknight. One Wednesday afternoon, I broke down and went to see Gone with the Wind in the theatre—by myself. It was busy with a mix of couples and single people. As I sat there silently watching the movie, I realized the only difference going by myself was that I had more time to observe the other people before the movie. That's the moment I knew movies weren't the social activity we've made them to be.

I enjoyed the remaining days of the retreat. On the last night after dinner, plaid shirt left. He made an excuse about getting home to his wife. I think the staff asked him to leave early; he wasn't a fit with the group. No one was sad to see him go; they didn't want the creepy guy there when we read our own stories of love, loss, and heartache. I didn't want him there either, even though I finally had the answer to the question: why I was still single. I had been too busy enjoying life.

About the Author
Christine Maier

Christine Maier was born with a cleft lip and palate, classified as learning disabled, and had over 20 surgeries. She's become an NYPD Sergeant, author, speaker, and the first female director of NYC Emergency Management Watch Command.

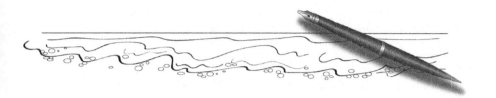

CATCH THE WIND

by

William John Rostron

It was ironic what song we would be playing when it all ended...when our world came crashing down. "Catch the Wind" was a haunting ballad of the 1960's which opined that seeking unreachable goals was like trying to catch the wind. For the five of us in a band named "Those Born Free," it was not just an image but a reality. Unfortunately, it was a reality that we just didn't realize until it was too late.

To use another musical metaphor, our "long and winding road" began innocently on a stickball court ten years prior. It was there that I met Gio and formed a friendship that was solidified by innumerable one-on-one matches of our favorite city game. As the years passed, we spent more time hanging out, often listening to music. It would be comical now if we had filmed our thirteen-year-old selves playing air guitar with our well-worn stickball bats.

It was Gio's idea to try the real thing, so we convinced our parents to buy us two $20 acoustic guitars from Sears. We self-taught ourselves some notes, which, when played, convinced us that the stickball bat guitars might actually create a better sound. However, eventually, we strung together a few chords and played a popular tune of the time, "Love Potion #9." We quickly had visions of appearing on stage.

"We've had a request for Love Potion #9."

"Oh, you want to hear it again?"

"And Again."

How far could our imagination carry us with a repertoire of only one song? Yet, we had visions of fame, fortune, and adoring female fans. It was then that fate intervened in the form of a Richie McCarthy fastball.

A high and tight pitch broke my left hand in a high school baseball game. Even after the cast came off, my fingers could not fit easily unto a guitar's frets and strings. One day in frustration, I went to a music store to see if other guitar brands might be easier to play. However, something made me pick up a bass guitar. Its thicker strings and different design made playing possible for my damaged hand. I immediately fell in love with the sound of the instrument. I convinced my parents to buy me that electric bass and amp. Gio likewise induced his parents to buy him an electric guitar. Still displaying no great talent, these purchases were acts of faith.

Soon, we could adequately play five songs (much louder now). It was time to fill out our band. Gio discovered a drummer in his woodworking class. The kid was pounding out the classic drum solo to "Wipeout" with two wooden dowels instead of using them to make the project that the teacher had in mind. It was a find. Jimmy Mac was the greatest drummer that I had ever seen. More than that, he had a great singing voice. Gio and Jimmy soon learned to sing beautiful harmony, and we knew we had something special. However, we still needed a lead guitar.

An old friend called and boasted that he played the organ and was looking for a group. As a bonus, he was also bringing a lead guitarist with him. The audition started well as we played a classic garage band song called "96 Tears." It was a song laced with a memorable but not complex organ riff. My friend Gary played the repetitious tune well, and when we finished, I had high hopes.

"Okay, what do you want to do next?" I asked expectantly. "Something by the Stones, or maybe the

Kinks?"

"No," was all he answered.

"How about Yardbirds, or maybe the Lovin' Spoonful?"

"No."

"Okay, what can you play?" I asked as inoffensively as possible.

He proceeded to play "96 Tears" again. He then explained that he had rented the organ and amp and memorized that one song. When pressed, he told us that he heard band guys got the girls and that he had had a particularly long cold streak in that area.

"So, what would you do if you actually got into a band?"

"Fake it."

I was going to react to the fact that he had tried to fool us. I then recalled the dreams that Gio and I had after we had learned one song and decided that Gary was a friend first and a failed musician second. The look on his face made me realize he understood this wasn't going to work out. I began to think that this had been a waste of time. I hadn't thought about the guitarist that Gary had brought along. He hadn't played much or, for that matter, even spoken much, his social skills a bit limited. I looked over

346

at him and then at Gary, who nodded at me.

"He's good...very good. You should hear him."

"Okay, let's see what you got," I mumbled skeptically. Gary smiled as his friend played. It took us only minutes to realize that we had ourselves a lead guitar.

I would find out later that this guitarist was a victim of abuse by his father. In those days, no one called social services or the police. It was a more "spare the rod, spoil the child" time, especially in blue-collar areas. When I asked him his name, he mumbled something that I could barely make out. I had to look at his guitar case to see the name Rocco Brackowski. Weird, I thought, an Italian first name and a Polish last name—and a mouthful to say. Gio didn't even try and dubbed him "Bracko," somehow combining and mutilating the poor guy's two names.

While attending Sunday mass the next day, I was distracted. All I could think of was the expectation of our upcoming practice. Yet, in the background of my consciousness was the driving sound of the church's massive organ. If only we could add that sound to our group. I excused myself and climbed over people in my pew. I found my way to the church's nave and the path to the balcony— the music's source. Looking back, I don't know why I did this. There was a good chance that the sound reverberating through the building was being

347

produced by a septuagenarian lady who would go home to her multiple cats after the final blessing.

To my surprise, a young guy I vaguely knew was playing the Hammond organ. I knew his name was Joseph Tinley, but not much else about him. Apparently, he spent all of his free time practicing the piano inside the confines of his home. His father was a music teacher and was determined that his son would gain admission to Julliard and pursue a career in classical music. Joseph (his father never allowed him to be called Joey) had no such plans and just played for the enjoyment. I think Joey (take that, Mr. Tinley) was thrilled at my offer yet realized he would have to confront his father and overcome his objections. Therefore, when our first practice arrived the following Saturday, we still didn't know if we were a quartet or a quintet.

As Joey/Joseph's father helped him unload his organ and amp from his car to Jimmy Mac's basement, the attitude of suspicion reeked from every pore of the elder Tinley. He said nothing and left. I tried to explain to the group that our new member was Joseph when his father was around and Joey when he wasn't. Gio just shook his head. Having dubbed Rocco Brackowski as Bracko, he now confronted the name discrepancy with Joseph/Joey Tinley.

348

"Screw that," chuckled Gio, "from now on, he's Tinman."

Misunderstanding Gio's reference to his last name, Joey answered back in anger. That was the first time I realized that there was more to this kid's personality. Obviously, he had many issues with his overbearing father and felt subjugated to his will. But, with us, he would speak up.

"Is that because you don't think I have a heart?" countered Joey, thinking that he was somehow being compared to the character from the Wizard of Oz. I had visions of the whole band dynamic crashing down around me before we even started. I was about to step in and calm the situation. However, Gio stepped up with his usual smile and easy manner.

"You know Tinley...Tinman. You're lucky. Look what I did to Rocco Brackowki over there. I made him Bracko. And James McAvoy became Jimmy Mac. Now, if you had an interesting handle like Giovanni, shortened to Gio, then we would have no problem. But you gotta understand, all our names need to sound cool on the album cover."

"What album cover?" questioned the newly named Tinman, sounding much calmer and agreeable.

"The best damn album ever made...the one we're going to make."

349

Sensing that the mood had lightened, I stuck in my two cents.

"So, if he's going to be Tinman, how about we call you Toto?" I barked at Gio—I mean, I literally barked.

The ice was broken that very first day. We had five excellent musicians, four of whom could sing exceptionally well. I was the exception. Gio used to say I sang like a dead frog. He then amended the statement to say, "No, a dead frog would sing better by virtue of being dead and therefore having no sound at all."

******

We spent the next year honing a unique style. We all subjugated our egos to the will of the entire group. And damn, we were great. I remember reflecting on that day when it all started...when Gio and I learned our first song, "Love Potion #9." How far we had come from that day. However, now the band was so good that I remember thinking that the music in and of itself was a reward. Before, our youthful goals had been different—fame, fortune, and girls. But now, our sound was so solid that I was tempted to broadcast to the world, "Forget the fame, forget the fortune, and forget the girls." Though I don't think I ever actually muttered (or thought), "Forget the girls!"

We bonded as musicians during that year of practices,

but perhaps more importantly, we bonded as friends. We knew what each of us brought to the table and why it was so crucial for us to succeed.

We learned that Bracko was abused and needed success to gain independence from the father who so savagely beat him. Tinman wanted a career in music—just not one in classical music as his father desired and planned for him. Jimmy Mac was slated to join the family candy store business. He loved his family but despised the concept of spending his life making egg creams and selling penny candies.

Me? I had a girlfriend about whom I was pretty serious (even at age 17) and thought that success would allow me to be with her over her family's very strong objections. On the other hand, Gio just wanted to be a star. However, at his core, he was like the rest of us. We knew that stardom would guarantee escape from our violent and drug-riddled neighborhood.

As we auditioned for a major career break, these thoughts flashed through my mind. After all our hard work, it had come down to one other band and us for a gig that would pay us well for playing four nights a week. Amazingly, it also included a contract to produce a record album. There was so much at stake.

I stood off in my usual location, a corner of the stage

on the very fringes of the house lights. I liked it that way. I didn't need the attention to be a part of what we had created. While the band nailed each song perfectly, I reflected on how far we had come and how far we could go.

As Bracko started to hit the first notes of our last song, "Catch the Wind," we all looked over at our manager, who gave us a thumbs up, signifying we had won the job. After that, I couldn't help but look at each of the faces of my bandmates...my friends. I couldn't know that it would be the last time we would ever perform.

I looked at Gio standing in the limelight, the frontman of the band, smiling and interacting with the audience. He basked in the glory as only my oldest friend could. "Gio, the superstar."

In contrast, Bracko's face held fresh bruises. We knew who had inflicted them. Droplets of blood ran down his chin from the cut opened on his lip only a few short hours before. As that same blood dripped onto his guitar, he played on with celebratory passion. He smiled as I had never seen him smile before. After tonight, he would never have to live with that madman again.

Tinman's organ sounded like a kaleidoscope of notes, and his facial expression revealed his love of the music he now played—something his father could never take away from him. Jimmy Mac's expression likewise related joy. There would be no egg creams in his future.

The song went on, building in volume and intricacy. This was the success that we dreamed about. The whole world now lay at our feet. Nothing would stand in our way of catching the wind.

Then it was over.

...the sounds of our voices and instruments silenced... lost forever in that wind.

******

Police officers appeared in the back of the club. It had been reported (by the losing band) that we were underage. We were. We had trusted that our manager would provide phony proof for us. He didn't. Each officer focused on a different band member as they waded through the crowd. Yet sheer math soon made the situation confused. There were four officers and five band members. In their zeal to control the situation, they had neglected me. I always performed on the fringe of the stage, which now offered me the opportunity to simply place my instrument down and step into the crowd. Gio smiled at my escape and gave me a thumbs up. Jimmy Mac, trapped behind his drums, pointed a stick at me and laughed. Tinman looked confused, and Bracko just didn't give a damn.

353

The laughing ended when each of them was taken into custody. I found my way to the bar, lifted an abandoned glass, and mingled with some customers who supported my deception. My life was changed forever.

******

The story above is true. On June 17, 1967, I was that bass player who slipped away into the crowd. I never saw the other band members after that day. I called Gio's house, and he advised me not to contact any of them in the immediate future. The group agreed that the police did not know about me, and he added, "Hey, dumbass, why should you go down if you don't have to?"

I tried to resume a veil of normalcy. The following week, while walking in a park on a date, I noticed a group of figures attacking a young boy. I ran towards them. I realized that I was being foolish. The ensuing decades have helped me understand why I acted so insane. The guilt and depression of not sharing my friends' fate had left me with a great deal of anger and self-loathing. I needed to do something to justify my singular survival of the situation.

Due to the damage suffered to my head, the subsequent events remain a blur. I know that I dragged the stranger to safety before passing out from the injuries sustained in my ill-advised rescue. Unfortunately, I don't remember much about my extended hospital stay. When I again walked the streets of my neighborhood, everything had changed. Gio had left the state, and I couldn't get the parents of the others to tell me anything. Eventually, I gave up and went on with my life.

I moved away, went on to college, got married, had children, and became a teacher—all the while wondering what had happened to the four of them. But I never forgot them. For thirty years, this lack of knowledge swirled in my mind. I imagined all kinds of scenarios. Then, finally, after decades of mystery, I tracked down Gio in Florida, 1300 miles from where we had had our childhood.

We talked well into the night about the good times, yet he shied away from what happened while I lay in the hospital. Finally, in 1999 with the onset of the internet, I emailed him and asked point-blank for details. His simple reply revealed so little...yet so much.

"The Driftwood Club was owned by the Mafia. They weren't happy." End of message.

The implications of his statement drove me insane. Yet he would give me no more. In early 2010, I set out to tell our story the only way I could...as fiction. I entitled the novel *Band in the Wind*. Reading this piece, you have become privy to a brief sketch of the actual events. Not knowing what transpired after the raid on the club, my imagination ran wild with what could have happened to the four members of a group we had called Those Born Free. That imagination is the substance of my written work.

With the popularity of my first book, I continued the story with two sequels, *Sound of Redemption* and *Brotherhood of Forever*. Therefore, in my fictional world, all the mysteries have been solved. Unfortunately, in my real world, there are no answers. Thus, the characters I named Bracko and Tinman remain enigmas. No amount of internet expertise can turn them up.

In late 2020, I found the person I named Jimmy Mac on Facebook. I sent innumerable messages to him with no response. Though his account remained active, he had passed away in 2013, ironically, on the exact day I had completed my first draft of *Band in the Wind*.

That only left "Gio." In 2019, he and his wife moved back to New York after half a century in Florida. He doesn't know of that change. He has early-onset dementia. He remembers me because I visit as much as possible. Unfortunately, he remembers very little else. So now there is no one to tell me the true story.

A few months ago, I brought him up to a room in my house where I keep my guitars. He quickly wrapped his fingers around the neck of my Fender in position to hit an

"A" chord, the first chord of "Love Potion #9." Then, I picked up my bass and was ready to join him in the song we first played half a century ago as young, excited teens.

His fingers dropped off the guitar, and as much as he tried, he could not remember where to put them again. I took the guitar and tried to refresh his memory. I played the first few notes of the song that *he* had once taught me.

"That's a nice song. Did that just come out?"

I cried.

I remembered the words to a song called "Get Together" that came out about the same time as our demise. Its lyrics were prophetic.

"We were but a moment's sunlight fading in the grass." I am the only one left to remember Those Born Free...a band lost forever in the wind.

About the Author
William John Rostron

William John Rostron is the author of a series of novels steeped in the music and culture of the mid to late 20th Century (Band in the Wind, Sound of Redemption, and Brotherhood of Forever). He recently published an anthology of short fiction, non-fiction, and "almost fiction" entitled "A Flamingo Under the Carousel." Four of these short pieces have been read and performed on stage in NYC by TV and Broadway actors. Viewed on www.WilliamJohnRostron.com

359

TIME OUT

by

Janet Rudolph

It was a hot sticky day as five of us followed a curving mountainous path to take in some nature. Our foreheads glistened and our shirts stuck to our back as we huffed and hurried, eager to be away from civilization.

As if in answer to our desire, the sky suddenly darkened, and the moist air turned cool. An embracing stillness descended. We had entered a circular grove of trees.

Each of us stood in hushed wonderment. The canopy of leaves completely obliterated the sun. Dark mists rose from the soil as the earthy smell of ferns and moss penetrated our consciousness. We understood instantly that this was the primordial moisture of birth, the ancient cauldron that cradles the seeds of life.

As we stood rooted to the ground, enthralled by the lushness, we began to hear the slow steady beat of a drum.

Was some ancient tribe celebrating life or was it the energy of the trees themselves, pulsing in response to our presence?

Our hearts beat in time with the rhythm surrounding us. The boundaries of ourselves and the trees dissolved and for a moment time stood still and we were one.

Then someone spoke out loud, reminding us of the 3:00 meeting we needed to attend. The spell was broken. Awkwardly, we stepped out of the grove into the heavy, humid, sun filled air.

About the Author
Janet Rudolph

I am a wife, lover, mother, grandmother, seeker, finder, air-breather, water-swimmer and more. I have two shamanic initiations and have written books including When Moses Was a Shaman and When Eve Was a Goddess. I write to express, heal, inform, challenge, startle and expand love.

mysticpagan.com

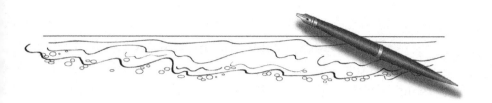

DIAMONDS ARE FOREVER - SOMETIMES

by

Lois Schmitt

It seemed to be a bargain. The ad read forty percent off and the salesclerk stated the clarity of the diamond in the ring was "near flawless." An independent appraisal given AFTER purchase, however, showed the diamond had several imperfections and was considerably less valuable than the salesclerk had claimed. Was the consumer able to get a refund?

Unfortunately, no. The receipt only gave the carat size and said nothing about clarity. Since what the salesman said was never written down, there was no proof.

The quality of the diamond ring you buy is up to you, but you should get what you pay for. Diamond value is based on the four Cs—carat, color, cut, and clarity. It is important to know what these terms mean and to make sure the salesperson's claim is written on the receipt or on the jeweler's appraisal at time of purchase.

CARAT – Most people are aware of carat weight when buying a diamond and often base their purchasing decision solely on this factor. This can be a mistake. One carat is divided into one hundred points, so a fifty-point diamond is half a carat or 0.5 carats. Two diamonds of equal carat size, however, can be of unequal value, depending upon the other factors.

COLOR – The color grading scale varies from totally colorless to light brown. Usually there is a subtle difference between one grade and the next one. For this reason, be wary of recessed or tract lighting at jewelry counters. This lighting is sometimes used to make the color difficult to see. To verify the color grade, also ask to be shown the stone against a master diamond.

Consumers who are not aware of the color grading can easily fall victim to advertising hype. One home shopping program described their diamond as *champagne color*. Sounds lovely? Champagne color is a fancy term for light brown—the lowest level in the color grading chart. Colorless is the highest. (NOTE: There are some colors not on the chart that are exceptions. Pink diamonds are among the most valuable in the world.)

CUT – Don't confuse cut with shape. The shape, be it pear, oval, or round, is a matter of personal preference. The cut of the diamond determines the amount of light that

366

the stone reflects back to the eye. When a diamond is cut to good proportions, light is reflected from one facet to another and then dispersed through the top of the stone, so it sparkles. If the cut is too deep or shallow, the light escapes before it can be reflected. The cut can change the value by as much as forty percent.

CLARITY- This has to do with imperfections. On the top of the list is flawless, which is extremely rare. At the bottom of the chart is "an imperfection that can be seen by the naked eye." Only in this category can you see without magnification, yet the difference between every ranking in- between can alter the diamond's value. For this reason, insist on looking at the diamond through a jeweler's loupe of at least ten percent magnification.

In addition to having details concerning the carat size, color, cut, and clarity spelled out on the receipt, there are other ways to protect yourself when buying diamond jewelry. Be wary of fantastic discounts, such as fifty percent off. Was the diamond originally priced at a ridiculously high amount just to make you think you are getting a bargain now? Shop around and compare, but make sure you compare the four Cs each time.

It is also important to deal with a reputable dealer. Look for someone who is a member of a professional organization such as Jewelers of America. Check for a complaint record with the department of Consumer Affairs in the county or city where the store is located.

Once you've purchased your diamond ring, you need to protect yourself against diamond switching. This doesn't happen frequently, but it does happen.

The best way to avoid this scam is to not let the ring out of your sight for cleaning, a new appraisal, or repair. When getting a diamond ring cleaned, make sure you watch the process. If the jeweler is too busy to do an immediate cleaning, take the ring back and make an appointment for a day when you can watch.

Unfortunately, if you decide you want to reset your ring, it can take time. In these cases, there are two steps you can take. If your diamond is certified and comes with a grading report, the stone should have a laser inscription engraved on the edge. This inscription can be read using a jeweler's loupe. The numbers and letters on the inscription should be the same as the one listed on the certificate.

If your stone is not inscribed, you should have it plotted.

A diamond plot is a map of all the imperfections (inclusions) in your diamond.

Plotting is like fingerprinting. Each stone's plot is unique—none are the same. If you have a plot, you can check that the diamond in the reset ring is the same stone that you provided.

Whether you are checking the inscription or verifying the diamond plot, you need to do this while you are still at the jewelers. If you leave and come back, there is no way to prove that the diamond you now have is the one the jeweler gave you back.

Remember, when dealing with diamonds, look beyond the glitter.

About the Author
Lois Schmitt

Lois Schmitt is the author of the "animal lover's mystery series." Her most recent book is *Playing Possum* which takes place in a wildlife refuge. Lois also authored *Smart Spending*, a consumer education book. Her article in this anthology involves a consumer issue. You can find out more about Lois at loisschmitt.com.

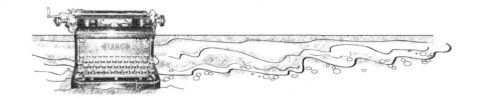

A FRESH NEW APPROACH
TO GETTING BOOK REVIEWS

by

Lois W. Stern

As authors, we all covet reviews for our books, but . . .

I don't know about you, but I'm fInding it more and more diffIcult to get them. What's an author to do? I just initiated a mini review writing contest for my *Tales2Inspire* books. I don't know if it's going to work, but I wanted to share it with you just in case, as some of you might want to adapt it for your own use and initiate your own mini review contest.

Here's my opening pitch:

Write a meaningful mini review (100 words or less) for any of the *Tales2Inspire* books. Add a catchy title and submit your mini review to this contest, along with the following.

A brief bio

373

Your headshot photo

URLs to any of your relevant links, (i.e., social media, website, etc.)

Optional: An object you would like to feature (If an author, one or a collection of your books would be great!)

"As an example, you can offer potential reviewers some enticing payoffs. For example:

If you have a blog, each month you can select one winner to post on your blog to highlight them for their achievement.

End each contest winner's review with an **About the Reviewer** section with the reviewer's bio, headshot and reviewer's preferred links included.

If you have a newsletter, feature the monthly contest winning reviewer in that as well.

You can use the free Canva program to create a personal banner for your monthly contest winner highlighting them, for them to use for their personal marketing purposes.

If you are replicating this project, try to connect with someone to work with you to select the winners and help spread the word, to lend authenticity to your project.

We will post winners' reviews on Amazon's Editorial

Reviews section (according to their guidelines), and that's a big deal. Here's why:

How an Editorial Review Helps the Reviewer

Although Amazon no longer counts Editorial Reviews toward the total number of reviews a book receives, those Editorial Reviews do something super good for the reviewer! Along with your review, we will include relevant credentials (i.e., author of, or other pertinent info). And as you already know, Amazon is a great place for wide exposure without costing you a dime.

Think of a way that you can honor your winners. Do you have a blog, website, newsletter, Twitter or Facebook page? Promise them some payoff and follow through.

If you can get a respected author or other person of note to select your monthly winner, it will add authenticity to your contest.

Tell your readers how to submit their mini reviews

Provide the name and email address of the person to whom the reviewer should submit their review.

Tell them to put words such as **Mini Review Contest** in the subject line.

Remind them to include the items listed above with their mini review:

Tips for Writing a Winning mini review

Write a catchy heading for your review in 10 words or less. **(HINT: Use strong words for your title as that is what other readers will see first, and sometimes the only part they read. So, make it pop!)**

Sincerity counts. Give the book the number of stars you think it deserves.

(1 is the lowest score, 5 is the highest. A 5-star rating means that you really liked the book, 4 stars means it was very good, 3 stars, just okay, etc.).

Answer a few of questions about this book to help you create your review. (I include Book Discussion Questions at the end of each of my *Tales2Inspire* books, but you can

376

always ask the author to send you some questions as suggestions of topics they would like you to address.)

End your review with your actual name, not a pseudonym. Readers will take more notice of your words if written by a person with an authentic name.

Finally, read over your review to correct any errors before submitting it.

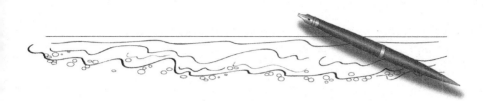

WELCOME TO THE THEATRE OF THE ABSURD

by

Lois W. Stern

I woke with a start to the sound of a clunk, followed in short order by an AH *Sh#! expletive... My hubby, Ken, was already downstairs, working on one of his handy man special projects.

"Ouch! My big toe. It's swelling to the size of a tomato. Quick. I need ice," he shouted.

I jumped out of bed, bounded down the steps two at a time, sideswiping Ken who now was hopping up and down, moaning pitifully. "Ice cubes," he shouted. In my haste to assist, I nearly toppled the poor man to the floor. But at the last second, he used his free hand, the one not wrapped around his sore toe, to grab the wall and regain his balance. "I need ice cubes," he wailed again.

I made a beeline for the freezer, plopped two fistfuls of ice cubes into a self-seal plastic bag and raced back to inspect Hubby's tomato-toe. "What's going on here?" I asked.

"I dropped that heavy duty hammer on my big toe. Look how swollen it is already."

If I were asked to take an oath, I'd say his toe was more the size of a strawberry, but who's to quibble over such a mundane thing as the comparative sizes of various fruits!

Ken's thunderous shouts had begun to settle into moans and groans. "Mom is visiting today, and I was planning to take her to the driving range. But there's no way I can do that now. I can't even stand up, no less swing a club. I'm not going anyplace today. I probably will have to sit here and ice my toe for the rest of the day."

"Why don't you do that for a while and see if the swelling goes down. Maybe we could do something fun with Mom and still keep you off your feet for most of the day," I suggested.

After fifteen minutes of agony, he decided that a good movie might be just the ticket. A rerun of an old movie we had seen years before was playing at an art theatre some distance from our home: *Trip to Bountiful*, a musical with strong characters and a warm fuzzy feel. "Mom would love that movie," I offered. "Actually, I think we'd even enjoy seeing it again. We can still make this into a good

380

day." Little did we know what was in store for all of us!

"I've got an idea," Ken said, placing a pair of soft suede moccasins into a shopping bag. "I'll wear these rubber beach sandals for driving but wear the moccasins to walk into the theatre. Then I can change back into the beach sandals after the lights dim. That way I can keep the pressure off my big toe for most of the day, but not look like a hippy in public."

And that's when the drama began. That shopping bag became the root of all our troubles.

In exchange for two crisp twenty-dollar bills, Hubby was handed three theatre tickets and a bit of change. But then the squinty-eyed woman seated behind the glass partition eyed the shopping bag and snarled, "You can't bring that in here." At first, we thought this gray-streaked, frizzy-haired theatre matron was joking, but the glare in her eyes told us otherwise.

Ken began a reasonable conversation as he opened the bag to share its contents. "You see, I injured my toe this morning and thought I'd be more comfortable if I wore these sandals during the movie."

She was unimpressed. "I said, you can't take that bag in my theatre."

"Well suppose I slip into the sandals now, put the

moccasins in this bag and leave them with you to pick up after the movie?" he offered.

Now the matron sprang into action. Leaning forward, she pushed both hands down onto the counter, narrowed her eyes, pressed her nose against the glass partition and shouted, "I said you can't take that bag in here - period. Now get out. I don't want you in my theatre." Next, she stood up, pivoted toward the back room, and whispered to an invisible someone, "This one is trouble."

Ken stared at her, speechless, then slowly straightened as he mentally donned his combat boots. As he regained his senses, he shifted to a contentious mood. "What do you mean, we can't come in here?" he said, warming up to the argument. "I certainly *am* coming into your theatre. I just bought three tickets and I intend to take my family inside to watch this movie."

"Oh-oh," I thought.

Right on cue, a dour-faced young woman burst into the lobby, waving her arms in increasingly rapid circular motions. Still flapping her wings, she stood in the foyer blocking our entrance into the theatre. "Any minute she's going to rise into the air," I thought.

My mother-in-law and I stood on the sidelines, mouths agape, stunned into silence. Hubby was not so quiet. He set his jaw, the muscles in his neck now pulsating. "This is

382

absurd," he barked while staring her down.

When another man appeared—I assumed he was the gray-haired matron's husband—he thrust those two crisps twenty-dollar bills back into my husband's hands; however, he was in no mood for reconciliation. Throwing the bills away, Hubby waved the tickets in the air. His red face matched the color of his swollen toe, and his voice spiraled up by two octaves.

"I never heard of such a ridiculous thing. This is absurd! How can you treat your patrons this way?" As his voice rose in crescendo, I watched in horror as I saw him curl his hand into a fist and I ran.

I darted out of the theatre like a woman possessed. I sprinted down the median of the busy road that fronted the establishment, waving my arms. "Please, help me," I begged, as the approaching cars zipped by. No one stopped. Finally, a police car appeared and pulled up to the curb. "My husband is about to commit a justified homicide! Please come stop him!" I pointed desperately toward the theatre.

The officer just shook his head and smiled. "Lady, those people are just plain crazy. But, since they own the theatre, they can make up their own rules."

"But my husband is so fired up. I've never seen him like this before. Please, even if you can't force them to let us see the movie, p-l-e-a-s-e come inside before they get really physical. If nothing else, just calm them down even if you can't force them to let us see the movie."

The man dressed in navy parked his blue and white Chevy and accompanied me back to the theatre. We could hear shouting as we neared the entranceway, but the appearance of the uniform seemed to quiet everyone down. The officer looped his arm around Ken's shoulder. "Come on outside. I have some stories about these people that will make your hair curl."

Ken's hand shot out as he snatched the two twenties from the theatre man's hand and tossed the tickets at his feet. Once we passed through the exit door, the officer regaled us with other crazy tales about the theatre owners. They denied access to a woman who was accompanied by her Seeing-Eye dog. Also, they forced a crowd of people to stand in a frigid downpour rather than allowing them access to the lobby area to wait for the ticket window to open. They even forced another woman to leave the theatre before she could read the rolling credits, as punishment for arriving a few minutes late. (Since they were the only three moviegoers in the audience, limited seating was hardly an issue.) His stories helped lighten the air.

We accompanied the policeman back to his car and watched him as he readied to leave. Then he turned to face us one last time. "Welcome to the theatre of the absurd," he winked, before sliding into the driver's seat to drive away.

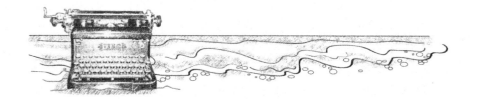

WHAT DOES IT REALLY TAKE
TO BE INSPIRING?

by

Lois W. Stern

Because of my attraction to inspiring stories, the Forbes Magazine headline, *What It Really Takes to Be Inspiring*, immediately caught my eye. I wanted to see if Forbes would agree with my definition of that word. The Forbes magazine article speaks about three core behaviors of deeply inspiring people.

Forbes Magazine identifies three key traits of inspiring people:

Inspiring people have forged their own authentic path. They have taken a hard, unpaved road. They demand a tremendous show of guts, strength, commitment, and perseverance. Ordinarily they are supremely "other-focused," deriving an enormous sense of satisfaction in helping other people. They spend most of their professional time and energy helping others, and feel personal rewards as they watch those people, organizations and enterprises grow and flourish. Finally, inspiring people are riveting storytellers. It wasn't until I read that article that I began to understand something about myself: What makes me tick.

That said, I have a few thoughts on what makes a story inspiring

To craft an inspiring story, overall, you have to allow the positive to shine through. Here are some ways to make that happen:

Show evidence of selfless giving and heartfelt emotions, whether your story revolves around an animal or person.

Share memoirs that awaken warm, fuzzy thoughts and emotions in others.

Tell humorous stories that bind people together to increase their happiness or intimacy.

Uplift the reader's spirits or give them an 'aha' moment of awareness.

Invite the reader in so they can experience the power of the message for themselves.

There are some sure-fire killers to inspiring your readers. My advice: Avoid them like the plague!

Don't tell your readers how to feel, live, think, etc. Instead of telling, let each reader feel it for themselves and draw their own conclusions.

Don't proselytize. Instead of preaching, share messages to which people of all beliefs can relate.

Take your time. Share your story with other writers. Ask them how you could improve it. Then listen and continue to polish your work.

Be careful not to meander or lose focus. Instead, stick to one central theme and develop it fully.

About the Author
Lois W. Stern

Lois' work has been featured in the *New York Times, Newsday, Long Island Press, Barnard Magazine,* on Local Access TV and in live presentations. She has published fifteen *Tales2Inspire®* anthologies. Readers can get a free *Tales2Inspire®* sampler book of six of her winners' stories at:

https://www.tales2inspire.com/gifts

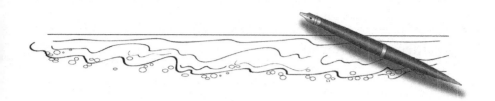

MY GRANDMOTHER'S HOUSE

by

Malve von Hassell

Childhood memories are strange beasts—fascinating, menacing, hated, and loved in turn. We pick at them as if they were scabs, unable to resist their lure. They are ingrained in our souls. And yet, they don't define us. When we claim them, we can transform them from dreaded ghosts into steppingstones.

As a child, I spent many holidays in my grandmother's house in a small village outside of Munich. My images from those days are as vivid as if I were watching a film.

Coming up from the garden below the house, where I had played in leaf piles in the abandoned swimming pool, I walked around the back past the living room. White gravel crunched under my feet. The cast iron chairs, tipped over like old women dressed in black lace and gossiping at a street corner, were covered with leaves. The garden doors were closed.

I could see the inkpot, letter opener, and dark green leather folder on my grandfather's desk. It always looked as if he was about to sit down to write; yet, he had died at the hands of the Gestapo years before I was born. My grandmother sometimes allowed us a brief glimpse of the memoirs he had written in prison. Bewildered and helpless, I would stare at the handwriting, familiar to me because it looked like my father's. But before we could ask questions, my grandmother would put everything away.

I passed by the bay window of my aunt's apartment, with a quick furtive look at the clutter inside, enough to evoke the dense air of stale cigarette smoke and heavy perfume. The apartment was stuffed with furniture, books and magazines on every surface, with overflowing ashtrays on top. We were rarely invited to visit our aunt in her domain. Dressed in black and holding a long black cigarette holder, she spoke to us in her deep hoarse voice before sending us away again.

It was time to go inside. I opened the heavy front door.

Silence loomed in the dark hallway, measured by the ticking of the grandfather clock. In the afternoon, everyone was taking a nap. Chinese dragon incense burners guarded the hallway. For a moment, I thought about the alcove in the dining room, where my grandmother kept dusty jars filled with a grayish yellow mess behind a brocade curtain. "It is a very special honey," she would say in a voice laden with mystery when she caught me peeking at the jars before pulling the curtain back. "It's called stone honey." I never got to eat it.

I avoided looking at the door to the basement or the door to the large room next to it, incomprehensibly filed with rows of tables and sewing machines. It seemed as if invisible people sat at the tables, bent over piles of fabric, their feet moving the pedals of the sewing machines. Years later, I learned that in the first years after the war, refugees, who lived in the house, labored in this room in a form of work from home instead of going to a workshop or factory. For reasons that escape me no one bothered to remove the sewing machines once the refugees had found housing.

My father's contribution to this half-imagined world was his reference to "Oblomov on the couch." For years, I was convinced that we had an odd relative called Oblomov who spent much of his time sleeping. I became rather fond of Oblomov, largely because my father spoke of him with such amused affection. In fact, it happened to be a hapless refugee of Russian extraction who resided there for a time, christened by my father after a character in a novel by the Russian writer Ivan Goncharov. Ilya Ilyich Oblomov was a young nobleman who rarely leaves his room or bed.

The kitchen door was closed; there the hunchbacked old cook washed dishes, bent over a huge slop sink. She used to give me slices of golden-brown honey cake and home-made elderberry juice in an enameled tin cup.

I crept up the staircase, past a huge etching showing the principal participants at the Congress of Vienna, yellowed and covered with water spots. On the landing, one door led to my grandaunt's apartment. Sometimes she invited my brothers and me for tea; invariably my grandmother would appear after a short time to interrupt and take us away, oblivious to my grandaunt's muttered grumblings of annoyance. Another door led to a portion of the attic where my grandaunt's elderly companion lived. There was not much space amidst trunks and a narrow bed, and even though she was tiny and frail, she had to bend over when she walked around so as not to hit the ceiling. When she wasn't preparing meals for my grandaunt which she carried down the narrow staircase on a tray, she worked on a sewing machine, undaunted by bad lighting. She had a bread mill, and I liked to sneak up there to turn the handle. Across the door to her attic, another led to the room where my parents stayed during our visits. Like all the other rooms, it held twin beds, a sink with chipped enamel, threadbare curtains, and a cast-iron stove with an old copper kettle that had not been used in years.

Dark mahogany furniture lined the walls of the long hallway, framing a marble bust of my grandfather. I passed the door of the cook's narrow one-room apartment. Two doors side by side led to drafty cubicles, each containing a toilet with a wooden toilet seat and a skylight that let in the night. In an alcove, hobby-horses and walking sticks with snakeheads crowded together in umbrella stands, shape-changing in the half-light of the afternoon. The bathroom held no terrors, only old-fashioned and reassuring discomfort —a rusted hot-water boiler on the wall, a large tub that was never used, drawers full of empty bottles, saved by my grandmother in case of another war, large, enameled pitchers used for carrying hot water to the bedrooms, and a wicker basket with shoe polish and brushes. Sometimes I opened it to breathe in the pungent smell.

Across from the bathroom was my grandmother's room. Her bed was buried in the back behind desks and tables piled with books, chests of drawers filled with letters and papers, worn easy chairs, and a screen behind which she washed and pinned up her long silvery hair, all overlaid by a faint scent of lavender.

The next door led up to the other half of the attic, dusty, warm, dry, and full of hidden life. It contained my grandaunt's dowry chests, piles of unframed etchings of battleships, Charlemagne, and the Virgin Mary, riding boots hanging from the ceiling, and sewing models, headless actors lost in the back wings of a theater. On rainy days, my brothers and I performed appendicitis operations on them.

We slept on twin beds with lumpy mattresses and comforters that bunched up like inflated sacks of four. I cannot remember the view from the windows. It seems that the house was always inward looking, content with itself and its own thoughts and dreams.

The room at the end of this hallway was round; from the outside that part of the house looked like Rapunzel's tower, the ivy doubling for her long braid. Crowded bookshelves underneath the bay windows, faded Persian carpets, and a black stove were a perfect setting for all those ghostly characters out of old stories—invariably cursing the owner of a castle and dying on the same spot, always to reappear at the stroke of midnight as a bundle of groaning, stinking, creaking rags that spoke in a scratchy voice. A toy stable, filled with hay, housed a slender horse with a silky beige coat and mane. The leather reins and the saddle felt smooth and soft to the touch. The horse's name was Grane. I neither knew nor cared that it was named after the steed ridden by Brunhilde the Valkyrie. The little horse with its velvet nose was a comforting friend, and I loved it.

It is all gone now. The old ladies in their relentlessly black clothes have died, the house is sold, and its contents are dispersed. Yet I still feel myself clutching my brother in the middle of the night, too frightened to walk down the long hallway to go to one of the toilets by myself. I still see myself sitting on a little stool, with a scrapbook, pictures, scissors, and glue, my brothers next to me with their projects, in my grandmother's room. Sitting in her easy chair underneath the portrait of the King of Hannover, she read ghost stories to us—her high old voice filled with excitement and anticipation. I still hear the grandfather clock ticking, holding me in its grip.

About the Author
Malve von Hassell

Malve von Hassell is a freelance writer and translator. Her publications include *The Falconer's Apprentice* (namelos, 2015), *Alina: A Song for the Telling* (BHC Press, 2020), and *The Amber Crane* (Odyssey Press, 2021), and *Tapestry of My Mother's Life: Stories, Fragments, and Silences* (Next Chapter Publishing, 2021.)

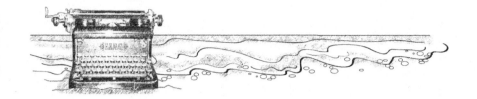

PANDEMIC

by

Robert J. Williams

It was as if gas was escaping from the oven in the way Ameir had said, "Daddy, do you want to know why my oxygen was low?" In a split second, I cut my eyes in his direction and lowered my head into position to listen.

A boy full of love, harmless and affectionate, had been broken, bandaged, and bruised in emotion. This was a story certainly for the news. At that point my mind and body moved as slow as a snail and I slugged my stiffened right leg from under the table. The gravity and weight of his words ping ponged through my head. I mean I was in shock, hand over mouth, jaw drooping. The words looped repeatedly. I finally was able to press pause; that's what trauma does. All the background noise began to fade. I almost exited the restaurant without paying. I was mentally between giving him immediate affection and attention. My eyes began to tear up. I no longer had a taste for food. My

403

voice dried up and began to crackle like fallen autumn leaves when you step on them. I choked up on words as I stepped away from the table. Now I had taken my son by his soft warm golden biscuit- colored hand, paired it with mine and exited the Chinese restaurant.

I was now drawn to return to the park, but the eyelids of the sky were closing in. Our day of fun and play ended sadly. The park is a safe spot for Ameir; it had been for the past several years. I looked at my son, the young Ameir, and I smothered, kissed, held and hugged him like any loving kind parent would do. I suddenly said to myself, if only I had been there to protect him. After listening to Ameir's testimony, it sounded as if Joanne had knocked the wind out of him. Here at this point I never understood why? Because he wasn't moving fast enough, so she suddenly snapped and allegedly plunged her knee into his tiny stomach as a means of punishment and discipline. It made me feel scared for him. As Ameir reenacted the traumatic event, visually showing in slow motion a gag reflex and how the impact of her knee knocked him to the floor. She then sat on top of him as he struggled to maintain his breathing. He relived the incident before me. I was shocked he had dropped this bomb on me. First thing I thought was, why you didn't tell me earlier, baby. As I thought about it, he did nonverbally. He and I did a pre–Father's Day photo shoot May 14, 2021, in Northport,

Long Island at the marina just four days after his eighth birthday. I sensed something was off about him during the photo shoot, although he was highly energetic, captivating and playing with other children. It wasn't until after Ameir unveiled the traumatic incident that I was able to establish this connection. My mind kept flashing back to the water, how he skipped across the big rocks and how he hung upside down from the tree and rolled down a steep hill. He was then trying to burn that horrible moment from his mind. No parent in their right mind wants to hear this unbearable news from an eight-year-old boy, then seven at the time of incident. Can you imagine the emotions that crossed my veins? Blooded and bonded in emotion and pain. It was like being trapped in a blazing fire where black smoked filled the room and you did all you could to get out. Yet you suffocated.

This momentous event triggered strong flashbacks of George Floyd's tragic death that left much of the world angered and upset. My own personal trauma. What a nightmare. What a horror. For a child to be loved by his father and hated by his mother. The indecent mistreatment of children often goes unseen or unheard. When one is recognized, and another goes unrecognized, we suffer from these checkerboard experiences. It is highly believed that some men do not have emotion or care to show it. I am not bullet proof. I am a man and a father, and I have

405

feelings and this fire will not be shut up in my bones or in my sons. I will continue to advocate and speak up for myself as well as for my son far beyond the realm of the court system. The courts provided the backboard and support for mothers to shoot. They shot wrong or right.

About the Author
Robert J. Williams

Robert Williams is a proud resident of the Wyandanch community. Writing has connected Williams to his purpose. He's able to channel the power of writing through poetry and prose. Writing has given Williams a voice, and he finds himself humble and expansive. Williams has become a vessel, an instrument to share personal incidents as well as a life changing near-death accident.

Made in United States
North Haven, CT
09 July 2022

21111401R00257